GEOMETRY PROOFS

Essential Practice Problems Workbook
with Full Solutions

Improve Your Math Fluency

Chris McMullen, Ph.D.

Geometry Proofs Essential Practice Problems Workbook with Full Solutions
Improve Your Math Fluency
Chris McMullen, Ph.D.

Copyright © 2019
Chris McMullen, Ph.D.
Cover design by Melissa Stevens
www.theillustratedauthor.net

www.monkeyphysicsblog.wordpress.com
www.improveyourmathfluency.com
www.chrismcmullen.wordpress.com

Zishka Publishing

ISBN: 978-1-941691-50-2

Textbooks > Math > Geometry
Study Guides > Workbooks> Math
Education > Math > Writing Proofs

CONTENTS

INTRODUCTION

This workbook is designed to help students practice writing geometry proofs. The early chapters review terminology, notation, and the underlying principles. Another chapter outlines the strategy and offers tips. Nine fully-solved examples are provided to help serve as a guide. Each of the exercises is fully solved in the back of the book.

This book focuses on plane Euclidean geometry. Standard topics are included, such as:

- parallel lines and transversals
- alternate interior angles
- similar and congruent triangles
- circles, chords, and tangents
- quadrilaterals
- the Pythagorean theorem
- regular polygons
- interior and exterior angles
- complements and supplements
- area of plane figures
- inscribed and circumscribed
- the centroid of a triangle

May you (or your students) find this workbook helpful and improve your fluency in writing geometry proofs.

TERMINOLOGY

A straight line extends infinitely in each direction.

A line segment is a portion of a straight line: it connects two points. The line segment is finite. It doesn't extend beyond its endpoints.

A ray has an endpoint at one side, but extends infinitely in the other direction.

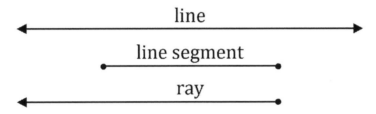

An angle forms when two lines intersect. (In this case, it doesn't matter if they are lines, line segments, or rays. Although if they are both lines, they technically form four angles.)

Angular measure refers to the numerical value that you would obtain (in degrees or radians) if you measured the angle with a protractor. Angular measure represents a number, whereas angle refers to a geometric figure (it is a visual representation).

A vertex is the point where two lines intersect. (In this case, it doesn't matter if they are lines, line segments, or rays.) The plural form of this term is vertices.

One degree is an angular measure corresponding to $\frac{1}{360}$ of a complete circle.

One radian is an angular measure defined such that π radians corresponds to 180°.

A right angle has an angular measure of 90°. One way to form a right angle is to draw one quarter of a circle.

An acute angle has an angular measure that is less than 90°.

An obtuse angle has an angular measure that is greater than 90°.

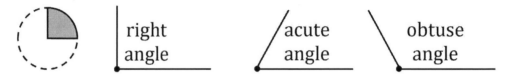

Parallel lines extend in the same direction and are the same distance apart at any position (such that they will never intersect).

Intersecting lines meet at some point. When only a portion of each line is drawn, you may need to imagine extending the lines in order to visualize the point of intersection.

Perpendicular lines intersect at a right angle. They form a 90° angular measure.

Two lines are askew if they are neither parallel nor intersecting. Two lines that lie in the same plane can't be askew, but it is possible for two nonplanar lines in space to be askew. (However, it is possible for two coplanar line segments to be askew. Recall that a line segment is finite, whereas a line extends infinitely.)

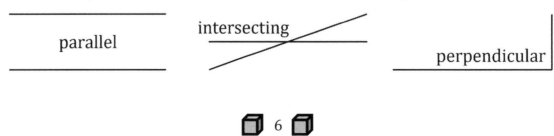

Complementary angles form a right angle. Their angular measures add up to 90°.

Supplementary angles form straight line. Their angular measures add up to 180°.

Vertical angles form on opposite sides of a vertex when lines intersect. Vertical angles are congruent.

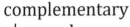

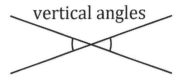

A plane is an infinitely large, flat, two-dimensional shape. Imagine an infinitely large rectangle (or even a circle) as that would form a plane.

A polygon is a closed plane figure with straight edges.

An equilateral polygon has sides with the same length.

An equiangular polygon has interior angles with the same angular measure.

A regular polygon is both equilateral and equiangular.

An interior angle forms at the vertex of a polygon and lies inside of the polygon.

An exterior angle is formed by one edge of a polygon and a line that extends from an adjacent edge.

For a convex polygon, the measure of all of the interior angles is less than 180°.

For a concave polygon, at least one interior angle is greater than 180°.

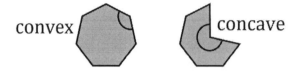

Some common polygons include the triangle (3 sides), quadrilateral (4 sides), pentagon (5 sides), hexagon (6 sides), heptagon (7 sides), and octagon (8 sides).

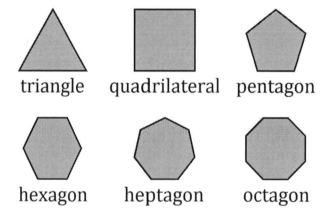

An isosceles triangle has two sides with the same length.

An equilateral triangle has three sides with the same length. An equilateral triangle is also equiangular (but this isn't necessarily true for other types of polygons).

A scalene triangle has sides with all lengths different.

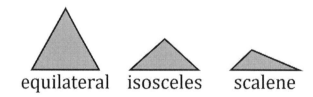

A quadrilateral is a polygon with four sides. Special quadrilaterals include the square (regular), rectangle (equiangular), rhombus (equilateral), parallelogram (two pairs of parallel edges), and the trapezoid (one pair of parallel edges).

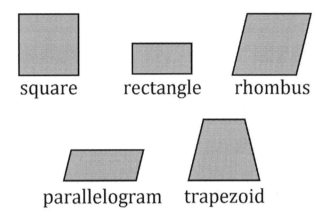

square   rectangle   rhombus

parallelogram   trapezoid

The term equidistant means equally distant.

The midpoint of a line segment is equidistant from the endpoints.

A median joins the vertex of a triangle to the midpoint of the opposite side.

A bisector cuts something into two equal parts. When the term bisector is applied to a line segment, it cuts the line segment in half. When the term bisector is applied to an angle, it cuts the angle in half. For a general triangle, note that the angle bisector isn't the same as the median. On the diagram below on the right, the solid line is the median (which bisects the right edge) while the dashed line is the angle bisector (it bisects the angle on the left).

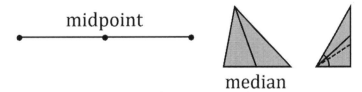

midpoint

median

A circle is a closed curve where each point on the curve is equidistant from the point in the center.

A radius is a line segment extending from the center to the edge of a circle.

A diameter is a line segment passing through the center of a circle which connects two points on opposite edges of the circle. The diameter is twice as long as the radius.

The circumference is the distance around the edge of a circle.

A line is tangent to a circle if it touches the edge of the circle only at a single point.

A line that touches the edge of a circle at two points is called a secant.

A chord is a line segment that connects two points on the edge of a circle. The chord that passes through the center of the circle is called the diameter.

An arc length is the distance around a portion of the circle.

A sector is a region enclosed by an arc and the radii that join to its endpoints.

A circular segment is a region enclosed by an arc and a chord (or secant).

A central angle is an angle formed by two radii.

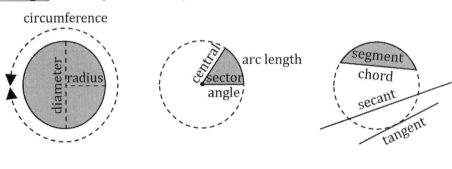

A polygon is inscribed in a circle when all of the polygon's vertices lie on the edge of the circle. Such a circle is circumscribed about the polygon.

A polygon is circumscribed about a circle when all of the polygon's edges are tangent to the circle. Such a circle is inscribed in the polygon.

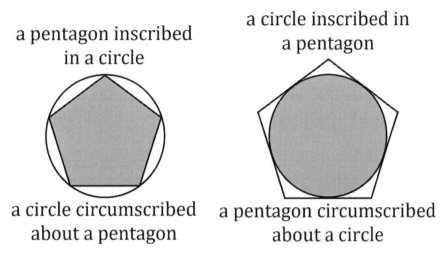

The centroid of a plane figure is the balancing point (or center of mass) of the figure (assuming that it is made of uniform material). For a triangle, the centroid lies at the point where the three medians intersect.

The perimeter of a polygon is the sum of the lengths of its edges.

A horizontal line runs left and right.

A vertical line runs up and down.

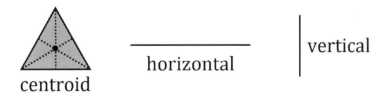

Two angles are congruent if they have the same angular measure. Two line segments are congruent if they have the same length. Two geometric figures (such as triangles) are congruent if they have the same size and shape (or they are mirror images).

Two geometric figures (such as triangles) are similar if they have the same shape, but not the same size. Note that similarity doesn't imply congruence.

A transversal is a line that intersects at least two lines.

When a transversal passes through two lines, alternate interior angles and alternate exterior angles form as shown below (there are two pairs of alternate interior angles and two pairs of alternate exterior angles). If the two lines are parallel, the alternate interior angles are congruent and the alternate exterior angles are also congruent.

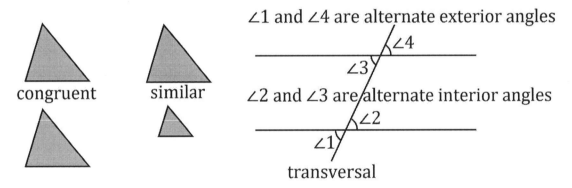

Two or more points (or lines or geometric figures) are coplanar if they lie in the same plane.

Two or more points (or line segments) are collinear if they are part of the same line.

Two points, lines, or geometric figures are coincident if they are one and the same.

The longest side of a right triangle is called the hypotenuse. It is the side opposite to the 90° angle.

The two shortest sides of a right triangle are called the legs. These sides are adjacent to the 90° angle.

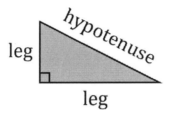

The constant pi (π) equals the ratio of the circumference of a circle to the diameter of the circle. It approximately equals 3.14159. It has the same value for any circle.

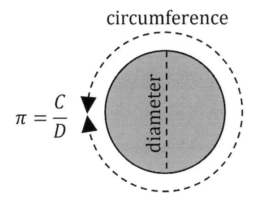

Angular measures may be expressed in degrees or in radians. One radian is defined such that π radians is equivalent to 180°. Some geometric formulas, like the equation for arc length, require the angular measure to be expressed in radians.

An axiom or postulate is a basic principle that is considered to be self-evident. The principle is accepted as true without any proof.

A theorem is a true mathematical statement that can be proven by applying various postulates (or other theorems already known to be true) using logic and reason.

A geometric proof applies logic, reason, given information, illustrations, definitions, postulates, and theorems already known to be true in order to draw a conclusion regarding a mathematical statement.

A corollary is another mathematical statement that follows from a proven theorem with very little effort.

A lemma is a helping theorem in the sense that the proof of the lemma helps to prove another more significant theorem.

Suppose that a mathematical statement has the form, "If A, then B."
- The converse of the statement has the form, "If B, then A."
- The inverse of the statement has the form, "If not A, then not B."
- The contrapositive of the statement has the form, "If not B, then not A."

If the original statement is true, then the contrapositive is also true. However, the converse and inverse may or may not be true. Logic and reasoning must be applied in order to determine whether or not the converse and inverse are true. See the examples at the end of Chapter 3.

The Use of Letters

- A single letter, like A or B, may refer to a single point.

$$A$$
•

- A pair of letters (with nothing above them), like AB or CD, is a length. It is the straight-line distance between the two points.

A ———— AB ———— B
•- - - - - - - - - - - - - •

- A pair of letters with a line (but not an arrow) over them, like $\overline{AB}$ or $\overline{CD}$, is a line segment connecting the two points.

A ———— $\overline{AB}$ ———— B
•————————————•

- A pair of letters with a single arrow over them, like $\overrightarrow{AB}$ or $\overrightarrow{CD}$, is a ray. The ray $\overrightarrow{AB}$ begins at point A, passes through point B, and continues forever. On the other side, it doesn't extend beyond point A. (Note that $\overrightarrow{BA}$ or $\overleftarrow{AB}$ extend from point B through and beyond point A, in contrast to $\overrightarrow{AB}$ or $\overrightarrow{BA}$.)

A ———— $\overrightarrow{AB}$ ———— B
•————————————•————————→

A ———— $\overrightarrow{BA}$ ———— B
←————————•————————————•

- A pair of letters with a double arrow over them, like $\overleftrightarrow{AB}$ or $\overleftrightarrow{CD}$, is a line (not a line segment). It passes through both points. The line extends infinitely in both directions.

A ———— $\overleftrightarrow{AB}$ ———— B
←————•————————————•————→

- Three letters together (without another symbol before them), like ABC, is a plane (which is infinite in size).

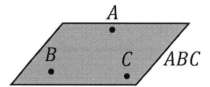

- When an angle ($\angle$) symbol comes before three letters (without an m before $\angle$), like $\angle ABC$, this represents the angle formed by the three points with the middle letter (in this example, B) at the vertex. This refers to the angle (but not the numerical measure of the angle). An alternative is to label angles like $\angle 4$ or $\angle \theta$.

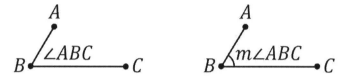

- When $m\angle$ comes before three letters, like $m\angle ABC$, this refers to the numerical measure of the angle. It represents a number in degrees or radians. An alternative is to label a measured angle like $m\angle 4$ or $m\angle \theta$.

- When a $\triangle$ symbol comes before three letters, like $\triangle ABC$, this represents a triangle.

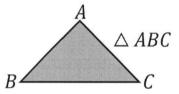

- When four or more letters come together, like $ABCD$, this refers to a region (such as a polygon) with corners at these points.

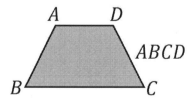

Equality, Congruence, and Similarity

- We use the equal sign ($=$) when numerical values are the same, but instead use the congruent sign ($\cong$) when two geometric figures are the same.
- The distance between two points, such as AB, is a numerical value. Angular measure, such as $m\angle ABC$, is a numerical value (in degrees or radians).
- A line segment, such as $\overline{AB}$, represents a geometric figure: it represents the line segment itself (whereas AB represents the distance between the points). An angle, such as $\angle ABC$, represents a geometric figure: it represents the angle itself, but not its numerical measure (whereas $m\angle ABC$ represents the angular measure of the angle as a number).
- $\overline{AB}$ and $\angle ABC$ refer to what is drawn, whereas AB and $m\angle ABC$ refer to what you would measure with a ruler or protractor. $\overline{AB}$ and $\angle ABC$ are visual, while AB and $m\angle ABC$ are numerical values.
- If the distances AB and CD are equal, we would write $AB = CD$. However, if we wish to make a similar statement about the line segments (rather than the distances), we would write $\overline{AB} \cong \overline{CD}$. The statement $AB = CD$ indicates that the lengths are equal, whereas statement $\overline{AB} \cong \overline{CD}$ indicates that the segments are congruent. The statement $AB = CD$ expresses equality between two numbers. The statement $\overline{AB} \cong \overline{CD}$ expresses the congruence of two figures.
- If the measured angles $m\angle ABC$ and $m\angle DEF$ have equal measure, we would write $m\angle ABC = m\angle DEF$. However, if we wish to make a similar statement about the angles (rather than the measured angles), we would write $\angle ABC \cong \angle DEF$. The statement $m\angle ABC = m\angle DEF$ indicates that the measured values of the angles are equal, whereas the statement $\angle ABC \cong \angle DEF$ indicates that the angles are congruent. The statement $m\angle ABC = m\angle DEF$ expresses equality between two numbers. The statement $\angle ABC \cong \angle DEF$ expresses the congruence of two figures.
- Triangles $\triangle ABC$ and $\triangle DEF$ may be congruent ($\triangle ABC \cong \triangle DEF$) or similar ($\triangle ABC \sim \triangle DEF$) as defined in Chapter 1, but they can't be equal ($=$).

Special Symbols

°	degree symbol
∠	angle
$m\angle$	the measure of an angle (in degrees or radians)
∟	right angle
△	triangle
◿	right triangle
■ (or □)	end of proof (the solid square stands out better in typography)
□	right angle (in a diagram where perpendicular lines intersect)
∥	parallel to
∦	not parallel to
⊥	perpendicular to
=	is equal to
≅	is congruent with
~	is similar to

≡	is identical to (alternative meaning: is defined as)
⇒	implies that
⇔	is equivalent to (alternative meaning: if and only if)
‒	line segment (when placed over a pair of letters)
↔	line (when placed over a pair of letters)
→	ray (when placed over a pair of letters)
∴	therefore
∵	because
:	such that (alternative meaning: ratio)
::	proportion
∀	for all
∃	there exists
∄	there doesn't exist
⋯	and so on (example: $1 + 2 + 3 + 4 + \cdots + N$)

Letters with Common Usage

θ	angle (lowercase Greek letter theta)
π	the ratio of the circumference of a circle to its diameter (called pi)
R	radius of a circle
D	diameter of a circle
h	height (if finding area) or hypotenuse (of a right triangle)
b	base of a triangle
w	width of a rectangle
L	length of a square or rectangle
A	area
P	perimeter
C	circumference of a circle
s	arc length

CONCEPTS

Vertical angles are congruent. This means that their angular measures are equal.

$$\angle 1 \cong \angle 3$$
$$\angle 2 \cong \angle 4$$

$$m\angle 1 = m\angle 3$$
$$m\angle 2 = m\angle 4$$

Perpendicular lines form four right angles when they intersect.

$$90° \quad 90°$$
$$90° \quad 90°$$

All **right angles** are congruent. The angular measure of any right angle equals 90°.

$$90°$$

Complementary angles form a right angle. This means that their angular measures add up to 90°.

$$m\angle 1 + m\angle 2 = 90°$$

Supplementary angles form a straight line. This means that their angular measures add up to 180°.

$$m\angle 1 + m\angle 2 = 180°$$

Angle sum theorem: the angular measures of the three interior angles of any triangle add up to 180°. See Proof #4 in Chapter 6.

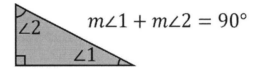

$$m\angle 1 + m\angle 2 + m\angle 3 = 180°$$

The two **acute interior angles of any right triangle** are complements. This means that their angular measures add up to 90°. See Proof #2 in Chapter 6.

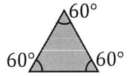

$$m\angle 1 + m\angle 2 = 90°$$

An **equilateral triangle** is necessarily equiangular. The angular measure of each interior angle of an equilateral triangle is 60°. This follows from the angle sum theorem, since $\frac{180°}{3} = 60°$.

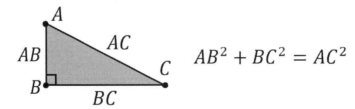

The **Pythagorean theorem**: the sum of the squares of the lengths of the two legs of any right triangle equals the square of the length of the hypotenuse. Be sure that you have a right triangle (which has a 90° angle) before applying the Pythagorean theorem. See Proofs #28-30 in Chapter 6.

$$AB^2 + BC^2 = AC^2$$

Triangle inequality theorem: the sum of the lengths of any two sides of a triangle is greater than the length of the remaining side. Note that this applies to all triangles. See Proof #13 in Chapter 6.

$$AB + BC > AC$$
$$BC + AC > AB$$
$$AC + AB > BC$$

The angular measure of an **exterior angle of any triangle** equals the sum of the angular measures of its two opposite interior angles. See Example #2 in Chapter 5.

$$m\angle 4 = m\angle 2 + m\angle 3$$

The angular measure of each **interior angle of a regular polygon** equals $180° - \frac{360°}{N}$, where N is the number of the polygon's edges. See Proof #7 in Chapter 6.

$$m\angle 1 = m\angle 2 = \cdots = m\angle N = 180° - \frac{360°}{N}$$

The angular measure of each **exterior angle of a regular polygon** equals $\frac{360°}{N}$, where N is the number of the polygon's edges. See Proof #8 in Chapter 6.

$$m\angle 1 = m\angle 2 = \cdots = m\angle N = \frac{360°}{N}$$

The sum of the angular measures of the interior angles of a polygon (even if the polygon isn't regular) equals 180°(N − 2), where N is the number of the polygon's edges. Note that this formula is for the sum of the angular measures. See Proof #5 in Chapter 6.

$$m\angle 1 + m\angle 2 + \cdots + m\angle N = 180°(N - 2)$$

The sum of the angular measures of the exterior angles of a polygon (even if the polygon isn't regular) equals 360°. Note that this is for the sum of the angular measures. See Proof #6 in Chapter 6.

$$m\angle 1 + m\angle 2 + \cdots + m\angle N = 360°$$

polygon	sum of the interior angular measures	sum of the exterior angular measures
triangle	180°	360°
quadrilateral	360°	360°
pentagon	540°	360°
hexagon	720°	360°

The angular measures of central angles forming one **full circle** add up to 360°. This follows from the definition that one degree corresponds to $\frac{1}{360}$ of a complete circle.

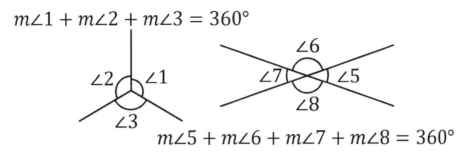

$$m\angle 1 + m\angle 2 + m\angle 3 = 360°$$

$$m\angle 5 + m\angle 6 + m\angle 7 + m\angle 8 = 360°$$

If a **transversal intersects two parallel lines**, the following statements are true. See Example #3 in Chapter 5 and Proof #3 in Chapter 6.

- Consecutive angles are supplementary (like ∠1 and ∠3 below).
- Corresponding angles are congruent (like ∠2 and ∠6 below).
- Alternate interior angles are congruent (like ∠3 and ∠6 below).
- Alternate exterior angles are congruent (like ∠2 and ∠7 below).

$$m\angle 1 = m\angle 4 = m\angle 5 = m\angle 8$$
$$m\angle 2 = m\angle 3 = m\angle 6 = m\angle 7$$
$$m\angle 1 + m\angle 2 = m\angle 3 + m\angle 4 = 180°$$
$$m\angle 1 + m\angle 3 = m\angle 2 + m\angle 4 = 180°$$
$$m\angle 5 + m\angle 6 = m\angle 7 + m\angle 8 = 180°$$
$$m\angle 5 + m\angle 7 = m\angle 6 + m\angle 8 = 180°$$

There exists a single **line** connecting two given points (that aren't coincident). There exists a single **plane** containing three given non-collinear points.

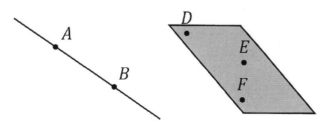

Four useful ways to demonstrate that two triangles are congruent are given below. (Note that AAA demonstrates similarity, but not congruence.)

- All three sides are congruent (SSS).
- Two sides and the angle formed by those two sides are congruent (SAS).
- Two angles and the side that touches both angles are congruent (ASA).
- Two angles and a side that doesn't touch both angles are congruent (AAS).

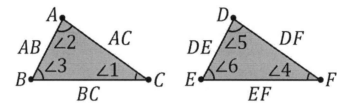

Two useful ways to demonstrate that two triangles are similar are given below. (For the first case, the third angle could be found from the angle sum theorem.)

- Two angles are congruent.
- All three sides come in the same proportions.

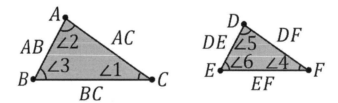

Corresponding parts of congruent triangles are congruent (CPCTC). This statement follows from the definition of congruence. If the two triangles shown below are known to be congruent, the CPCTC can be applied to justify any of the following:

$$\angle 1 \cong \angle 4 \ , \ \angle 2 \cong \angle 5 \ , \ \angle 3 \cong \angle 6 \ , \ \overline{AB} \cong \overline{DE} \ , \ \overline{BC} \cong \overline{EF} \ , \ \overline{AC} \cong \overline{DF}$$

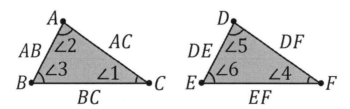

Corresponding edges of similar triangles come in the same proportions.

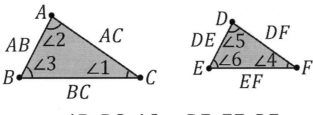

$$AB:BC:AC = DE:EF:DF$$

For a given line and a point that isn't on the line, within the plane containing the line and point there exists exactly one line that passes through the given point and which is parallel to the given line. Within the plane containing the line and point, there also exists exactly one line that passes through the given point and which is perpendicular to the given line. The line segment which connects the given point to the given line perpendicular to the given line is the shortest possible connector. See Proof #11 in Chapter 6.

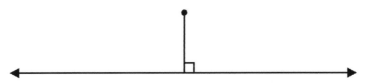

If two lines intersect, they intersect at a point and there exists exactly one plane containing these lines. If two planes intersect, they intersect at a line.

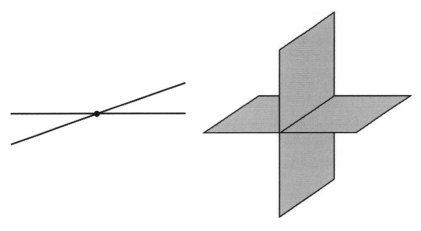

The parallel postulate: If a transversal intersects two lines (within a plane) and the two interior angles on the same side (so these are **not** alternate interior angles) don't add up to exactly 180°, then the two lines intersect on the side where the sum of the two interior angles is less than 180°. On the other hand, if the two interior angles on the same side do add up to 180°, then the two lines must be parallel.

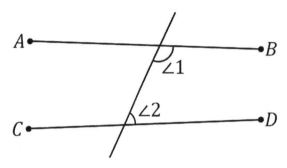

If $m\angle 1 + m\angle 2 < 180°$, then $\overleftrightarrow{AB}$ and $\overleftrightarrow{CD}$ intersect to the right.
If $m\angle 1 + m\angle 2 > 180°$, then $\overleftrightarrow{AB}$ and $\overleftrightarrow{CD}$ intersect to the left.
If $m\angle 1 + m\angle 2 = 180°$, then $\overleftrightarrow{AB}$ and $\overleftrightarrow{CD}$ are parallel.

Perpendicular bisector equidistant theorem: Any point that lies on the perpendicular bisector of a line segment is equidistant from the endpoints of the line segment. See Proof #12 in Chapter 6.

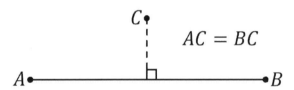

$AC = BC$

Triangle bisector theorem: The line that bisects an angle of a triangle divides the opposite edge of the triangle into segments in proportion to the lengths of the other two sides, according to the formula shown below. (A consequence of the triangle bisector theorem is that the angle bisector of a triangle is **different** from the median unless the two sides adjacent to the bisected angle are congruent.) See Proof #9 in Chapter 6.

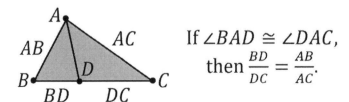

If $\angle BAD \cong \angle DAC$, then $\dfrac{BD}{DC} = \dfrac{AB}{AC}$.

A right isosceles triangle is one-half of a square. The angular measures of its interior angles are 45°, 45°, and 90°. The hypotenuse is $\sqrt{2}$ times longer than each leg. If you know that the two legs of a right triangle are congruent or if you know that a right triangle has a 45° angle, the following formulas may help you solve for the lengths of any remaining sides. If you know that the sides of a triangle come in the ratio $1:1:\sqrt{2}$, the interior angles have angular measures of 45°, 45°, and 90°.

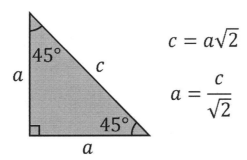

$$c = a\sqrt{2}$$

$$a = \frac{c}{\sqrt{2}}$$

A 30°-60°-90° triangle is one-half of an equilateral triangle. The angular measures of its interior angles are 30°, 60°, and 90°. The shorter leg is opposite to the 30° angle, the longer leg is opposite to the 60° angle, and the hypotenuse is opposite to the 90° angle. The hypotenuse is twice as long as the shorter leg. The longer leg is $\sqrt{3}$ times as long as the shorter leg. If you know that a right triangle has a 30° or 60° angle, the following formulas may help you solve for the lengths of any remaining sides. If you know that the sides of a triangle come in the ratio $1:\sqrt{3}:2$, the angle opposite to the shorter leg has an angular measure of 30°, the angle opposite to the longer leg has an angular measure of 60°, and the angle opposite to the hypotenuse (which is the longest side) is a right angle.

$$c = 2a \qquad c = \frac{2b}{\sqrt{3}} \qquad a = \frac{c}{2}$$

$$b = a\sqrt{3} \qquad b = \frac{c\sqrt{3}}{2} \qquad a = \frac{b}{\sqrt{3}}$$

If you know that two triangles are both right triangles, a few ways to show that the two right triangles are congruent are given below. These follow by applying the rules for showing that two triangles are congruent.

- Both legs are congruent.
- The hypotenuse and a corresponding leg are congruent.
- The hypotenuse and a corresponding acute angle are congruent.
- A leg and a corresponding acute angle are congruent.

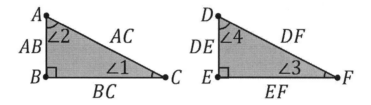

If you know that two triangles are both right triangles, a couple of ways to show that the two right triangles are similar are given below. These follow by applying the rules for showing that two triangles are similar.

- An acute angle is congruent.
- The two legs come in the same proportions.
- The hypotenuse and a corresponding leg come in the same proportions.

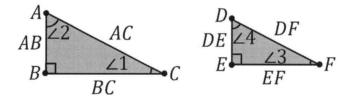

The angles opposite to the two congruent sides of an isosceles triangle are congruent. See Proof #10 in Chapter 6.

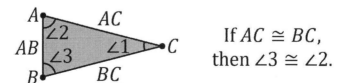

If $AC \cong BC$, then $\angle 3 \cong \angle 2$.

Following are a variety of concepts relating to quadrilaterals.

- One way to show that a quadrilateral is a parallelogram is to show that both pairs of opposite sides are congruent. Another way is to show that one pair of opposite sides are congruent and are also parallel. Any two consecutive interior angles of a parallelogram are supplementary.

- One way to show that a quadrilateral is a rectangle is to show that three of the interior angles have an angular measure of 90°. Another way is to show that the two diagonals are congruent.

- One way to show that a quadrilateral is a rhombus is to show that all four edges are congruent. Another way is to show that the diagonals are perpendicular. The diagonals of a rhombus also bisect the interior angles.

- A square satisfies the criteria for a rectangle as well as a rhombus. A square has equal edge lengths as well as 90° interior angular measures.

- One way to show that a quadrilateral is a trapezoid is to show that one pair of edges are parallel. (One common definition of a trapezoid also requires that the second pair of edges not be parallel.)

- If a four-sided polygon doesn't have any pairs of parallel edges, it is a general quadrilateral. It isn't a trapezoid, parallelogram, rhombus, rectangle, or square.

- The two diagonals of any parallelogram bisect one another's lengths.

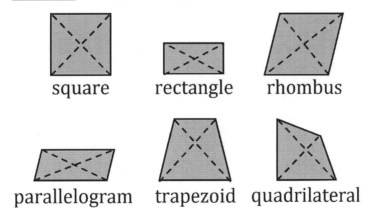

square   rectangle   rhombus

parallelogram   trapezoid   quadrilateral

Distances, angular measures, and areas obey the rules of arithmetic. For example, if line segment $\overline{AC}$ is divided into two shorter line segments $\overline{AB}$ and $\overline{BC}$, the length of the longer line segment equals the sum of the lengths of the shorter line segments: $AC = AB + BC$. As another example, if $\overline{DE} \cong \overline{FG}$ and $\overline{HI} \cong \overline{JK}$, then it follows that $DE + HI = FG + JK$. The similar rules for subtraction for these examples are $AB = AC - BC$ and $DE - HI = FG - JK$. The rules for multiplication and division apply as well. The notion that "the whole is greater than the part" follows from these rules.

The transitive rule applies to geometry. For example, if it is known that $\angle 1 \cong \angle 2$ and that $\angle 1 \cong \angle 3$, it follows that $\angle 2 \cong \angle 3$ and that $m\angle 2 = m\angle 3$. The reflexive property: Line segments (or angles or areas) that coincide are congruent.

The perimeter of a polygon equals the sum of the lengths of its edges.

$$P = AB + BC + CD + DE + EA$$

If the edge length of a square equals L, its area equals L^2. For example, consider a square with an edge length equal to one yard. Its area equals one square yard. To find its area in feet, you would use the fact that one yard equals three feet. This divides the square into a 3 ft. by 3 ft. square, consisting of 9 smaller squares (each with an area of one square foot), agreeing with the formula $A = L^2 = 3^2 = 9$ ft.^{2}

The area formulas for some common polygons are tabulated below.

triangle		$A = \dfrac{1}{2}bh$
square		$A = L^2$
rectangle		$A = wh$
parallelogram		$A = bh$
rhombus		$A = Lh$
trapezoid		$A = \left(\dfrac{a+b}{2}\right)h$

A line that is tangent to a circle is perpendicular to the diameter of the circle.

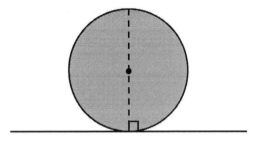

The perpendicular bisector of a chord passes through the center of the circle.

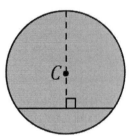

If two chords are equidistant from the center of the same circle, the two chords are congruent and their corresponding arc lengths are also congruent.

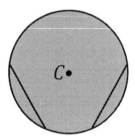

The formulas for the circumference and area of a circle are given below.

$$C = \pi D \qquad A = \pi R^2$$

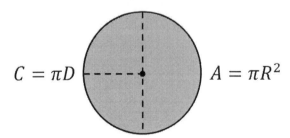

Angular measure may be expressed in degrees or radians (except for a few equations like the arc length formula, which require angular measure to be expressed in radians). Note that 180° and π radians are equivalent (since each corresponds to a semicircle).

$$\pi \text{ rad} = 180°$$

The diameter is twice the radius. The arc length is related to the central angle by the following formula, provided that θ is expressed in radians. See Proof #40 in Chapter 6.

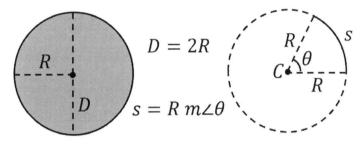

$$D = 2R$$

$$s = R\, m\angle\theta$$

Inscribed angle theorem: an angle inscribed in a circle has an angular measure equal to one-half of the angular measure of the central angle that intercepts the same arc length. See Proofs #43-44 in Chapter 6.

$$m\angle\alpha = \frac{m\angle\theta}{2}$$

If two angles inscribed in the same circle intercept the same arc length, then the two inscribed angles are congruent. This follows from the inscribed angle theorem.

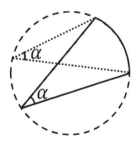

Thales's theorem: if a triangle is inscribed in a circle such that one side of the triangle is a diameter, the angle opposite to the diameter is a right angle. See Proof #45 in Chapter 6.

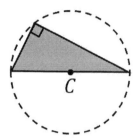

Tangent-chord theorem: the angle between a chord and a line that is tangent to the circle at one of the chord's endpoints has an angular measure that is one-half of the central angle formed by the chord. See Proof #46 in Chapter 6.

$$m\angle\alpha = \frac{m\angle\theta}{2}$$

Intersecting chords theorem: If two chords intersect, the four line segments formed by the point of intersection satisfy the following formula (which involves multiplying distances). See Proofs #48 and #49 in Chapter 6.

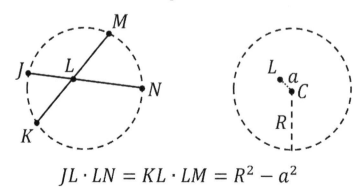

$$JL \cdot LN = KL \cdot LM = R^2 - a^2$$

The angle between two intersecting chords has an angular measure that is equal to the average of the angular measures of the central angles formed by the chords. See Proof #50 in Chapter 6.

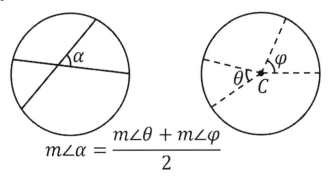

$$m\angle\alpha = \frac{m\angle\theta + m\angle\varphi}{2}$$

Intersecting secants theorem: If two secants intersect outside of a circle, the four line segments formed by the point of intersection satisfy the following formula (which involves multiplying distances). See Proofs #52 and #53 in Chapter 6. (If instead the two secants intersect inside of the circle, see the intersecting chords theorem.)

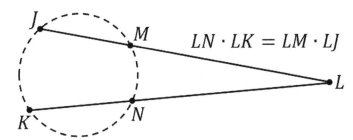

$$LN \cdot LK = LM \cdot LJ$$

The angle between two intersecting secants has an angular measure that is equal to one-half of the difference in the angular measures of the central angles formed by the secants (if the secants intersect outside of the circle). See Proof #54 in Chapter 6.

$$m\angle\alpha = \frac{m\angle\theta - m\angle\varphi}{2}$$

The contrapositive of a true statement is always true, but the converse and inverse may or may not be true. (These terms are defined at the end of Chapter 1.) You must use logic and reasoning to determine if the converse or inverse of a statement (or a theorem) are true. For example, consider the statement, "All right triangles have two acute angles," and the statement, "All triangles have three sides." These statements may be cast in the form, "If a triangle is a right triangle, it has two acute angles," and, "If a polygon is a triangle, it has three sides." Both statements are true.

- The contrapositive of the first statement is, "If a triangle does not have two acute angles, it is not a right triangle." The contrapositive of the first statement is true. The contrapositive of the second statement is, "If a polygon does not have three sides, it is not a triangle." The contrapositive of the second statement is also true. It can be proven that the contrapositive of *any* true statement is true.

- The converse of the first statement is, "If a triangle has two acute angles, it is a right triangle." The converse of the first statement can be proven false because a triangle with an obtuse angle has two acute angles and isn't a right triangle. The converse of the second statement is, "If a polygon has three sides, it is a triangle." The converse of the second statement is true because a three-sided polygon is a triangle. These examples show that the converse of a true statement isn't necessarily true.

- The inverse of the first statement is, "If a triangle is not a right triangle, it does not have two acute angles." The inverse of the first statement can be proven false because a triangle that is obtuse isn't a right triangle, but an obtuse triangle has two acute angles. The inverse of the second statement is, "If a polygon is not a triangle, it does not have three sides." The inverse of the second statement is true because a polygon with more than three sides isn't a triangle. These examples show that the inverse of a true statement isn't necessarily true.

Following are some tips and general advice for writing two-column proofs.

1. **Read** the problem carefully. Study any given diagrams thoroughly.
   - Read every word of the entire problem.
   - Circle or underline what you believe will be helpful information.
   - Identify key words like "isosceles" or "regular."
   - Beware that numbers may be written like "double" or "none."
   - What, exactly, is the problem asking you to prove or disprove?
2. Identify the **given** information. You will most likely need it in your proof.
   - Some of the information may be given in a sentence, like $\sqrt{3}$.
   - Other information may be labeled in a diagram, like 45°.
   - Look for helpful geometry terms like "equilateral" or "median."
3. Draw and label a **diagram**. This is like a flashlight that helps you see better.
   - If a diagram is already provided, study it carefully.
   - Beware that most diagrams are **not drawn to scale**.
   - Don't try to "guess" whether angles or distances "look" like they are congruent. Instead, apply rules of geometry to be "sure."
   - You may need to add on to any diagram that is already provided.
   - If a diagram isn't provided, draw your own.
   - Label the given information in the diagram.
   - As you determine new information, draw and label that as well.
4. Identify **complements** and **supplements** where possible.
   - If a right angle is divided into two angles, they are complements.
   - If two angles form a straight line, they are supplements.

5. Are there any **vertical angles**?
    - Whenever two lines intersect, they create two pairs of vertical angles.
    - Vertical angles are congruent.
    - It may help to extend a line segment to see the intersection better.

6. Identify any **parallel** lines or **perpendicular** lines.
    - Look for keywords like "parallel," "perpendicular," or "right."
    - Look for the right angle symbol (□) in a given diagram.
    - Can a postulate or theorem help you show that two lines are parallel or perpendicular?
    - Don't assume information that isn't made clear or that you can't prove.
    - If there are two lines that you know are parallel and the lines are cut by a transversal, it may help to apply a theorem (such as congruent alternate interior angles).
    - If you know that two lines are perpendicular, these lines create four 90° angles. If a right angle is divided into two angles, those angles are complements.

7. Look for distances and angles that may be **congruent**.
    - Look for key words like "isosceles," "regular," and "equilateral."
    - Vertical angles are congruent.
    - An angle bisector creates congruent angles, but a median may not.
    - A median (or bisector that isn't an angle bisector) creates equal lengths.
    - Don't assume information that isn't made clear or that you can't prove.

8. Are there any special **triangles**?
    - Each angle of an equilateral triangle has an angular measure of 60°.
    - If there is a right triangle, you may apply the Pythagorean theorem.
    - A 45° right triangle has sides in the ratio $1:1:\sqrt{2}$. A 30°-60°-90° triangle has sides in the ratio $1:\sqrt{3}:2$. You may be able to use the ratio to solve for an unknown side.
    - A square cut along its diagonal results in two 45° right triangles. An equilateral triangle cut along a median results in two 30°-60°-90° triangles.

- Can you show that a triangle is a right triangle? If not, can you form a right triangle (by drawing a line, for example)? It may help to apply the Pythagorean theorem to relate the lengths of a right triangle.

9. Are there any special **quadrilaterals**?

- A regular quadrilateral is a square. It has congruent edge lengths and its interior angles have angular measures of 90°.
- A rectangle has interior angles with angular measures of 90°.
- A rhombus has congruent edge lengths.
- A parallelogram (which includes the square, rectangle, rhombus, and a more general parallelogram) has two pairs of parallel edges.
- A trapezoid has one pair of parallel edges.

10. Are there **two triangles** (or two other plane figures)?

- Try the four tests for congruent triangles: SSS, SAS, ASA, and AAS.
- If you know that both triangles are right triangles, apply the tests for the congruence of right triangles (see Chapter 3).
- Once you know that two triangles are congruent, it may help to apply the CPCTC (explained in Chapter 3).
- If two triangles aren't congruent, test to see if they may be similar. Are two angles congruent? Do the sides come in the same proportions?
- Once you know that two triangles are similar, you know that they have congruent interior angles and that the sides come in the same proportions.

11. Does the problem involve a **circle**?

- Identify the center of the circle. Note that any line segment that connects the center of the circle to its edge is a radius.
- Identify chords, tangents, secants, and arc lengths. Note that if a chord passes through the center of the circle it is a diameter.
- It may help to draw a radius or diameter on a diagram. For example, if a tangent is drawn, the tangent is perpendicular to the diameter that intersects it.

12. Does the problem involve finding **area**?
    - It may help to apply one of the formulas from Chapter 3.
    - Note that polygons can be divided up into simpler shapes. For example, a parallelogram can be split into two triangles and a trapezoid can be divided into a rectangle and two triangles.
    - The addition rule states that the area of a region equals the sum of the areas of the non-overlapping parts of the region.

13. Examine the **terminology** involved in the problem.
    - It is often helpful to apply the definition of a term.
    - It may help to review the definitions from Chapter 1.

14. Can you apply any of the **concepts** or **equations** from Chapter 3?
    - It may help to browse through Chapter 3 for relevant information.
    - There are a variety of handy formulas in geometry, such as interior or exterior angular measures of polygons, perimeter of a polygon, area of polygons or circles, arc length, circumference, the Pythagorean theorem, inscribed angles, and intersecting chords or secants.

15. Organize your ideas logically in a **two-column proof**.
    - The left column contains mathematical statements, like $\overline{AB} \cong \overline{CD}$, $AB + CD = EF$, $\angle ABC \cong \angle DEF$, $m\angle ABC + m\angle DEF = 90°$, or $A = \pi R^2$.
    - The right column justifies each statement from the left column. It may state that information was given, follows from a definition, applies one of the postulates, uses a rule of algebra, or follows from a theorem.
    - At least one step will generally apply a concept, formula, or theorem from Chapter 3.
    - Each step should follow naturally and logically from the previous step.
    - Beware that the converse of a statement isn't necessarily true (see the last page of Chapter 3). Be careful when applying the converse.
    - The first step usually states given information or follows from a definition. The last line of the proof should result in what the problem asks you to prove.

16. Use **notation**, symbols, and abbreviations that are common in geometry.
    - It will help to be familiar with the notation and symbols from Chapter 2.
    - Note the distinction between AB (for a distance), $\overline{AB}$ (for a line segment), and $\overleftrightarrow{AB}$ (for a line).
    - Note the distinction between $\angle ABC$ (visual) and $m\angle ABC$ (a number), and similarly between $\angle 1$ and $m\angle 1$.
    - Use $\cong$ to express congruence (of line segments, angles, or triangles), but use $=$ to express equality (of distances or measured angles).
    - Some common words may be abbreviated (like def. for definition).
    - Some common phrases may be abbreviated, especially for important theorems. Examples include SAS (side angle side), PT (the Pythagorean theorem), and CPCTC (corresponding parts of congruent triangles are congruent).

17. It may help to review the **examples** in Chapter 5.
    - These examples illustrate how to write a proof.
    - Think your way through the examples so that you understand the logic and reasoning involved.
    - Strive to learn how to write statements in the left column and reasons in the right column, how to use symbols and abbreviations, and how to apply concepts from Chapter 3.

18. Students become better at writing proofs through **practice**.
    - The more problems you solve, the better.
    - Solve a wide variety of problems.
    - Try to solve the problem on your own before you check your answer.
    - When you finish solving a problem, check the solution in the back of the book. If you made a mistake, try to learn from it.

19. Approach the problem with **confidence** and open-mindedness.
    - Be determined to figure it out. Try very hard not to give up.
    - If you have studied and worked hard, use this to help feel confident.
    - If you solve some problems correctly, let this boost your confidence.

Following is a summary of the strategy.

1. Read the problem and study any given diagrams carefully.
2. Identify the given information.
3. Draw and label a diagram (beyond what is already drawn in the problem).
4. Look for complements and supplements.
5. Look for vertical angles.
6. Look for parallel lines and perpendicular lines.
7. Look for distances and angles that may be congruent.
8. If there is a triangle, is it one of the special triangles?
9. If there is a quadrilateral, are any pairs of edges parallel?
10. If there are two triangles (or other plane figures), apply tests for congruence or similarity.
11. If there is a circle, identify common features.
12. If you are finding area, look up common formulas. For a polygon, try to divide the given shape up into triangles and rectangles.
13. Check the definitions of the terms used in the problem.
14. Look for relevant concepts, theorems, and equations from Chapter 3.
15. Organize your ideas logically in a two-column proof.
16. Use notation, symbols, and abbreviations that are common in geometry.
17. It may help to review the **examples** in Chapter 5.
18. Try to feel confident, open-minded, and determined.
19. If you need help, check the hints at the end of the book.
20. When your proof is complete (or you just feel stumped), check the solution at the back of the book. Try to learn from any mistakes that you may have made.

Get the Most out of These Examples

- A math book doesn't read like a novel. Try to think your way through the examples. Take your time. Read each mathematical statement or explanation slowly.

- Try to understand the logic behind each statement or explanation before moving onto the next. Strive to understand how each statement follows from the previous statement.

- Before you read the explanation in the right column, try to predict what it will say. Before you read the next step, try to predict which step will come next in the proof.

- As you read the problem, circle or underline key information.

- After you read the problem and study the diagram, spend some time thinking about how you would try to solve it before you read the proof.

- Consider how each proof applies concepts, postulates, theorems, or equations from Chapter 3. In the problems, you will be applying material from Chapter 3. Sometimes, the concepts, postulates, theorems, or equations will differ from the examples. You want to learn how to decide which material is relevant for your proof. Beware that some problems may apply the same concept, postulate, theorem, or equation from an example in a different way. The more you understand the logic and reasoning, the easier it will get to apply material.

- Imagine trying to explain the proof to someone else. Attempting to explain a solution to somebody else often helps you understand it better.

- Consider different ways that the problem could be varied. That is, try to come up with other problems that are similar, but not quite the same. For each one, spend some time thinking about how you would solve the problem.

Example #1. In the diagram below, line segment $\overline{AB}$ is congruent with line segment $\overline{CD}$. Prove that line segment $\overline{AC}$ is congruent with line segment $\overline{BD}$.

$$A \quad\quad B \quad\quad\quad\quad\quad C \quad\quad D$$

❶ $\overline{AB} \cong \overline{CD}$.	❶ Given.
❷ $AB = CD$.	❷ Def. of congr. applied to Step 1.
❸ $AB + BC = CD + BC$.	❸ Add BC to both sides of Step 2.
❹ $AB + BC = AC$.	❹ Prop. of addition.
❺ $CD + BC = BD$.	❺ Prop. of addition.
❻ $AC = BD$.	❻ Sub. Steps 4-5 into Step 3.
❼ $\overline{AC} \cong \overline{BD}$. ∎	❼ Def. of congr. applied to Step 6. ∎

Notes:
- $\overline{AB}$ is a line segment, whereas AB is the length of the line segment.
- Line segments (like $\overline{AB}$ and $\overline{CD}$) can be congruent. Distances (like AB and CD) can be equal. Use $\cong$ for congruence and $=$ for equality.
- Step 3 applies the addition rule of algebra.
- Steps 4-5 apply the principle that distance is additive. Study the diagram to convince yourself of these equations.
- Def. = definition, congr. = congruence, prop. = property, sub. = substitute.
- ∎ = end of proof.

Example #2. Prove that the angular measure of an exterior angle of a triangle equals the sum of the angular measures of its two opposite interior angles.

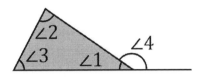

❶ $m\angle 1 + m\angle 4 = 180°$.

❷ $m\angle 1 = 180° - m\angle 4$.

❸ $m\angle 1 + m\angle 2 + m\angle 3 = 180°$.

❹ $180° - m\angle 4 + m\angle 2 + m\angle 3 = 180°$.

❺ $-m\angle 4 + m\angle 2 + m\angle 3 = 0$.

❻ $m\angle 2 + m\angle 3 = m\angle 4$. ■

❶ $\angle 1$ and $\angle 4$ are supplements.

❷ Subtract $m\angle 4$ from both sides of Step 1.

❸ Angle sum thm. for a triangle.

❹ Sub. Step 2 into Step 3.

❺ Subtract 180° from both sides of Step 4.

❻ Add $m\angle 4$ to both sides of Step 5. ■

Notes:

- $\angle 1$ is the angle itself, whereas $m\angle 1$ is its angular measure; $\angle 1$ is visual, while $m\angle 1$ is numerical.
- We replaced $m\angle 1$ with $180° - m\angle 4$ going from Step 3 to Step 4.
- 180° cancels out in the subtraction from Step 4 to Step 5.
- Thm. = theorem, sub. = substitute.

Example #3. The top and bottom lines shown below are parallel. Prove that angle ∠1 and angle ∠3 (which are corresponding angles) are congruent.

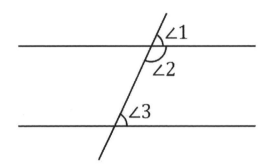

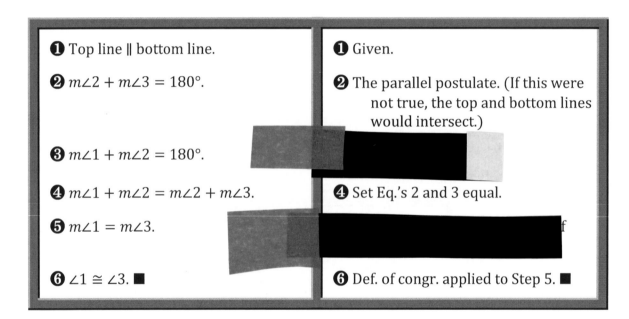

❶ Top line ∥ bottom line.

❷ $m\angle 2 + m\angle 3 = 180°$.

❸ $m\angle 1 + m\angle 2 = 180°$.

❹ $m\angle 1 + m\angle 2 = m\angle 2 + m\angle 3$.

❺ $m\angle 1 = m\angle 3$.

❻ $\angle 1 \cong \angle 3$. ■

❶ Given.

❷ The parallel postulate. (If this were not true, the top and bottom lines would intersect.)

❹ Set Eq.'s 2 and 3 equal.

❻ Def. of congr. applied to Step 5. ■

Notes:

- ∥ = parallel.
- ∠1 is an angle (visually), whereas $m\angle 1$ is its angular measure (numerically).
- Angles (like ∠1 and ∠3) can be congruent. Angular measures (like $m\angle 1$ and $m\angle 3$) can be equal. Use ≅ for congruence and = for equality.
- Suppl. = supplementary, eq. = equation, congr. = congruence.

48

Example #4. Prove that the edges of a 45° right triangle come in the ratio $1:1:\sqrt{2}$.

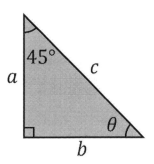

❶ The ang. meas. of one angle is 45°.	❶ Given.
❷ The ang. meas. of one angle is 90°.	❷ Def. of right triangle.
❸ $90° + 45° + \theta = 180°$.	❸ Angle sum thm.
❹ $\theta = 180° - 90° - 45° = 45°$.	❹ Solve for θ in Step 3.
❺ The triangle is isosceles.	❺ Two angles are congr.
❻ $b = a$.	❻ Prop. of isosc. triangle.
❼ $a^2 + b^2 = c^2$.	❼ P.T.
❽ $a^2 + a^2 = 2a^2 = c^2$.	❽ Sub. Step 6 into Step 7.
❾ $a\sqrt{2} = c$.	❾ Squareroot both sides of Step 8.
❿ $\dfrac{b}{a} = 1$ and $\dfrac{c}{a} = \sqrt{2}$. ∎	❿ Divide Steps 6 and 9 by a. ∎

Notes:
- The angles opposite to the congruent sides of an isosceles triangle are congruent. See Proof 10 in Chapter 6. The converse is also true.
- Def. = definition, thm. = theorem, prop. = property, P.T. = Pythagorean thm.

Example #5. Prove that angles $\angle BAD$ and $\angle DCB$ (which are opposite interior angles of the parallelogram shown below) are congruent.

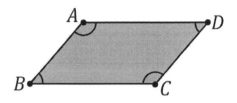

❶ $\overline{AD} \parallel \overline{BC}$ and $\overline{AB} \parallel \overline{CD}$.

❷ $m\angle BAD + m\angle ADC = 180°$.
$m\angle ADC + m\angle DCB = 180°$.
$m\angle DCB + m\angle CBA = 180°$.
$m\angle CBA + m\angle BAD = 180°$.

❷ The parallel postulate. (If these were not true, the pairs of lines coinciding with opposite edges would eventually intersect.)

❸ $m\angle BAD + m\angle ADC$
$= m\angle ADC + m\angle DCB$.

❹ $m\angle BAD = m\angle DCB$.

❹ Subtract $m\angle ADC$ from both sides of Step 3.

❺ Def. of congr. applied to Step 4. ∎

Notes:

- $\parallel$ = parallel.
- A parallelogram has two pairs of parallel edges.
- Note that the middle letter indicates the vertex of the angle. For example, A lies at the vertex of $\angle BAD$ whereas C lies at the vertex of $\angle DCB$.
- It could similarly be shown that $\angle ADC \cong \angle CBA$, which demonstrates that the opposite interior angles of a parallelogram are congruent.
- Def. = definition, eq. = equation, congr. = congruence.

Example #6. A parallelogram is cut into two triangles as shown below. Prove that the two triangles are congruent.

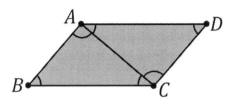

❶ $\overline{AD} \parallel \overline{BC}$ and $\overline{AB} \parallel \overline{CD}$.	❶ Def. of parallelogram.
❷ $\angle BAC \cong \angle DCA$.	❷ Alt. int. angles.
❸ $\angle BCA \cong \angle CAD$.	❸ Alt. int. angles.
❹ $\overline{AC}$ is common to both triangles.	❹ Reflexive prop.
❺ $\triangle BCA \cong \triangle CAD$. ∎	❺ ASA (Steps 2-4). ∎

Notes:
- $\parallel$ = parallel.
- A parallelogram has two pairs of parallel edges.
- Line segment $\overline{AC}$ is a transversal.
- Note that the middle letter indicates the vertex of the angle. For example, A lies at the vertex of $\angle BAC$ whereas C lies at the vertex of $\angle BCA$.
- The reflexive property states that distances which coincide are equal.
- ASA = angle side angle (for proof of congruence). Steps 2-4 showed that one side and its two adjacent angles of each triangle are congruent. From ASA, it follows that the two triangles are congruent.
- It follows from the CPCTC that opposite edges of a parallelogram are congruent.
- Def. = definition, alt. = alternate, int. = interior, prop. = property.

Example #7. Prove that the area of a triangle is one-half its base times its height.

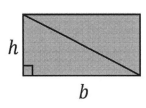 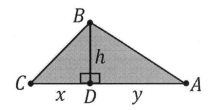

❶ A rectangle can be divided into two congruent triangles.

❷ The area of a right triangle is $\frac{1}{2}bh$.

❸ Any triangle can be divided into two right triangles.

❹ The areas of ΔBCD and ΔABD are $\frac{1}{2}xh$ and $\frac{1}{2}yh$.

❺ The area of ΔABC is $\frac{1}{2}xh + \frac{1}{2}yh$.

❻ The area of ΔABC is $\frac{1}{2}(x+y)h$.

❼ The base of ΔABC is $b = x + y$.

❽ The area of ΔABC is $A = \frac{1}{2}bh$. ■

❶ We proved this in Example 6 for a more general parallelogram.

❷ From Step 1, divide the area of a rectangle by 2.

❸ This is shown above. If the triangle is obtuse, put the obtuse angle at the top.

❹ Apply Step 2 to each right triangle. The bases are x and y.

❺ Add the formulas from Step 4. The area of a region equals the sum of the areas of its non-overlapping parts.

❻ Factor out $\frac{1}{2}h$ from Step 5.

❼ Prop. of addition.

❽ Sub. Step 7 into Step 6. ■

Notes:

- The addition rule applies to lengths and areas. This is why the area of a region equals the sum of the areas of its non-overlapping parts.
- Prop. = property.

Example #8. In the diagram below, point C lies at the center of the circle and the two tangent lines intersect at point A. Prove that $m\angle\alpha = \frac{m\angle\theta - m\angle\varphi}{2}$.

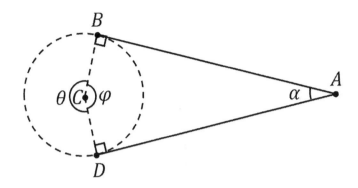

❶ BC and CD are radii.

❷ Angles $\angle ABC$ and $\angle ADC$ are right angles.

❸ $m\angle\alpha + 90° + m\angle\varphi + 90° = 360°$.

❹ $m\angle\alpha + m\angle\varphi = 180°$.

❺ $m\angle\theta + m\angle\varphi = 360°$.

❻ $\frac{m\angle\theta + m\angle\varphi}{2} = 180°$.

❼ $m\angle\alpha + m\angle\varphi = \frac{m\angle\theta + m\angle\varphi}{2}$.

❽ $m\angle\alpha = \frac{m\angle\theta - m\angle\varphi}{2}$. ∎

❶ Def. of radius.

❷ Tangent lines are perpendicular to the radius (or diameter).

❸ Int. angles of a quad.

❹ Subtract 180° from both sides of Step 3.

❺ The angular meas. of central angles forming a full circle sum to 360°.

❻ Divide both sides of Step 5 by 2.

❼ Set Eq.'s 4 and 6 equal.

❽ Subtract $m\angle\varphi$ from Step 7. ∎

Notes:

- $\frac{m\angle\theta + m\angle\varphi}{2} - m\angle\varphi = \frac{m\angle\theta + m\angle\varphi}{2} - \frac{2m\angle\varphi}{2} = \frac{m\angle\theta + m\angle\varphi - 2m\angle\varphi}{2} = \frac{m\angle\theta - m\angle\varphi}{2}$.

- Def. = definition, int. = interior, quad. = quadrilateral, meas. = measure.

Example #9. A quarter circle is drawn below. Prove that the area of the segment (shaded below) corresponding to the chord AB is given by the formula $A = \frac{\pi - 2}{4} R^2$.

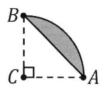

❶ The area of the 1/4 circle is $\frac{1}{4}\pi R^2$.

❷ BC and AC are radii.

❸ The area of $\triangle ABC$ is $\frac{1}{2}R^2$.

❹ The area of the segment (A) plus the area of the triangle equals the area of the quarter circle.

❺ $A + \frac{1}{2}R^2 = \frac{1}{4}\pi R^2$.

❻ $A = \frac{1}{4}\pi R^2 - \frac{1}{2}R^2$.

❼ $A = \frac{1}{4}\pi R^2 - \frac{2}{4}R^2 = \frac{R^2}{4}(\pi - 2)$.

❽ $A = \frac{\pi - 2}{4}R^2$. ∎

❶ Divide the area of a circle by 4.

❷ Def. of radius.

❸ Plug $b = R$ and $h = R$ into $\frac{1}{2}bh$.

❹ The area of a region equals the sum of the areas of its non-overlapping parts.

❺ Step 4 expressed algebraically.

❻ Subtract $\frac{1}{2}R^2$ from both sides of Step 5.

❼ Write $\frac{1}{2} = \frac{2}{4}$ and factor out $\frac{R^2}{4}$.

❽ Rules of algebra. ∎

Notes:

- The way to subtract fractions is to find a common denominator.
- Recall from algebra that $\frac{x}{y}z = x\frac{z}{y} = \frac{xz}{y}$.
- Def. = definition.

Get the Most out of These Exercises

- Review the strategy from Chapter 4.
- Study the examples from Chapter 5.
- Look up the definitions of terms used in Chapter 1.
- Follow the notation of Chapter 2.
- Be familiar with the concepts, postulates, theorems, and formulas in Chapter 3.
- Try to solve the problem by yourself first.
- Circle or underline key information stated in the problem.
- It may help to add to the given diagrams. It may also help to draw additional diagrams.
- Don't be afraid to test out an idea and see where it leads. The worst that can happen is that you may need to cross it out and start over. But it might turn out to be the right idea. You'll never know unless you try.
- If you feel that you are stuck, consult the Hints section at the back of the book (before checking the Solutions section). A little hint may be all you need.
- Enter mathematical statements in the left column.
- Write explanations in the right column.
- Number the steps of your proof in each column.
- When you finish solving a problem, compare your solution with the solution given at the back of the book.
- If you make any mistakes, try to learn from them. Everybody makes mistakes when they are learning. Good problem-solvers learn to avoid mistakes that they have made in the past.

Proof #1. In the diagram below, angle $\angle BAC$ is congruent with angle $\angle DAE$. Prove that angle $\angle BAD$ is congruent with angle $\angle CAE$.

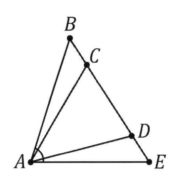

Proof #2. Prove that the two acute interior angles of a right triangle are complements.

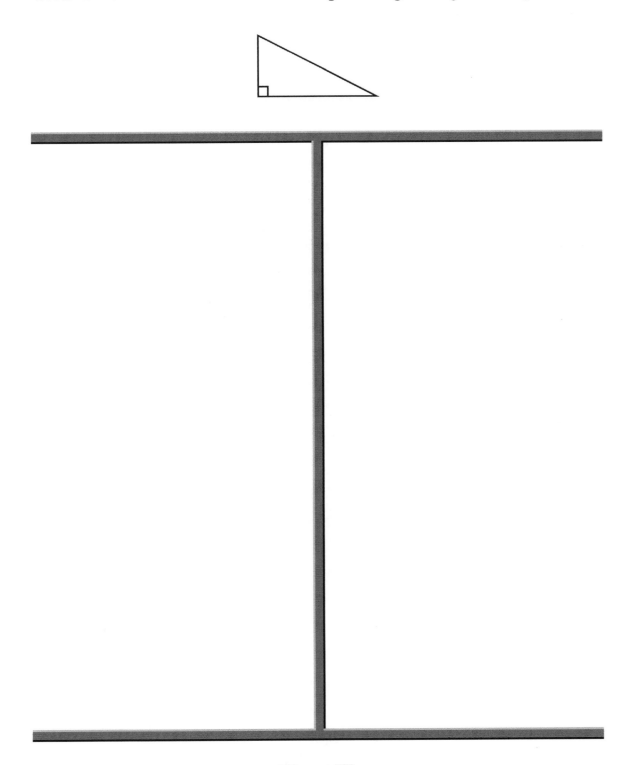

Proof #3. The top and bottom lines shown below are parallel. Prove that angle ∠1 and angle ∠2 (which are alternate interior angles) are congruent.

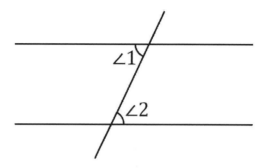

Proof #4. Use the diagram below to prove that the angular measures of the interior angles of a triangle add up to 180°. The top line is parallel to the base of the triangle. (Don't use a formula for an *N*-sided polygon.)

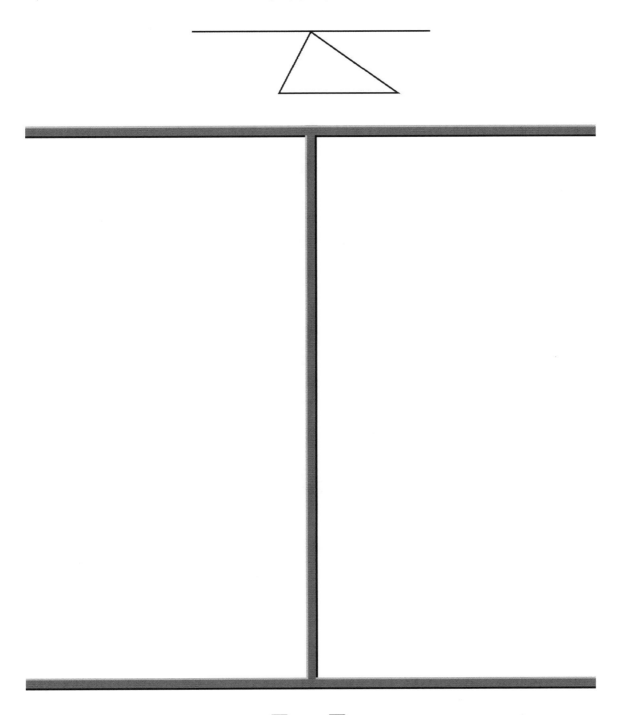

Proof #5. Prove that the sum of the angular measures of the interior angles of a polygon with N sides is equal to $(N - 2)180°$ (even if the polygon is irregular).

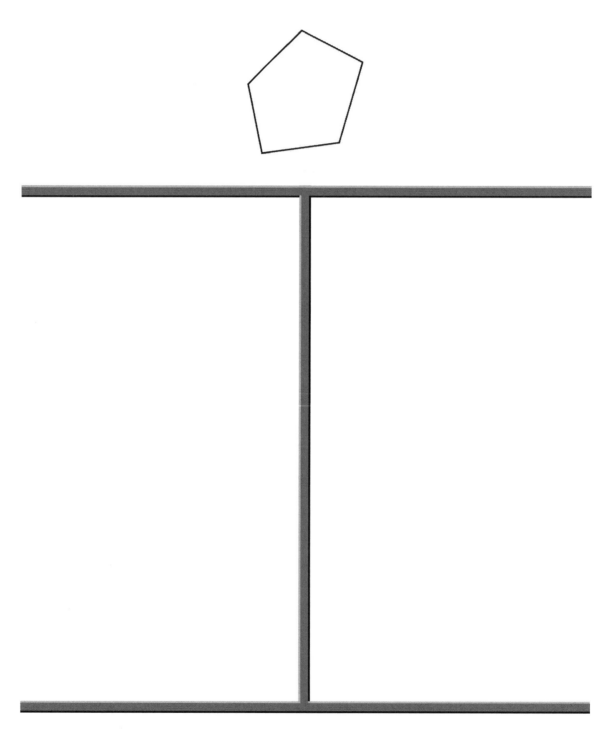

Proof #6. Prove that the sum of the angular measures of the exterior angles of a polygon with N sides is equal to $360°$ (even if the polygon is irregular).

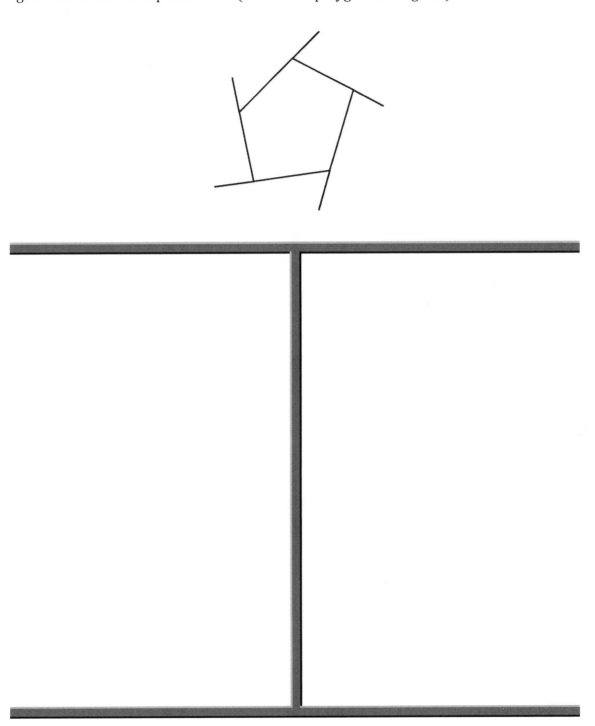

Proof #7. Prove that the angular measure of each interior angle of a regular polygon with N sides is equal to $180° - \frac{360°}{N}$.

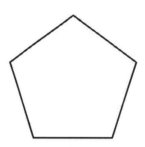

Proof #8. Prove that the angular measure of each exterior angle of a regular polygon with N sides is equal to $\frac{360°}{N}$.

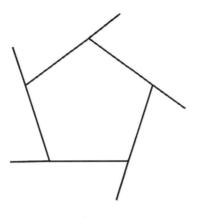

Proof #9. In the diagram below, segment $\overline{AE}$ is an angle bisector, meaning that angles $\angle BAE$ and $\angle EAC$ are congruent. Segments $\overline{BD}$ and $\overline{CF}$ are perpendicular to $\overline{AF}$. Prove the triangle bisector theorem, which states that $\frac{BE}{CE} = \frac{AB}{AC}$.

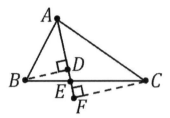

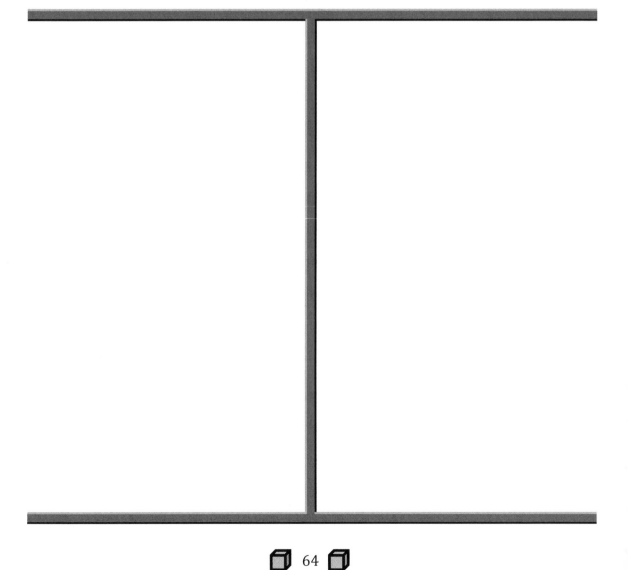

Proof #10. In the diagram below, triangle $\triangle ABC$ is isosceles with $\overline{AB}$ and $\overline{BC}$ congruent. Segment $\overline{BD}$ bisects $\overline{AC}$. Prove that angles $\angle BAD$ and $\angle BCD$ are congruent.

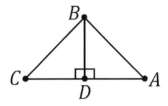

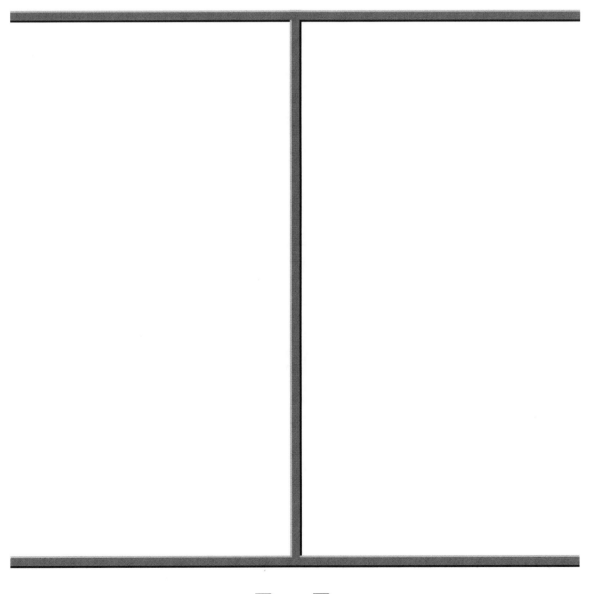

Proof #11. In the diagram below, line segment $\overline{AB}$ is perpendicular to the horizontal line. Prove that $\overline{AB}$ is the shortest possible segment that connects point A to the line.

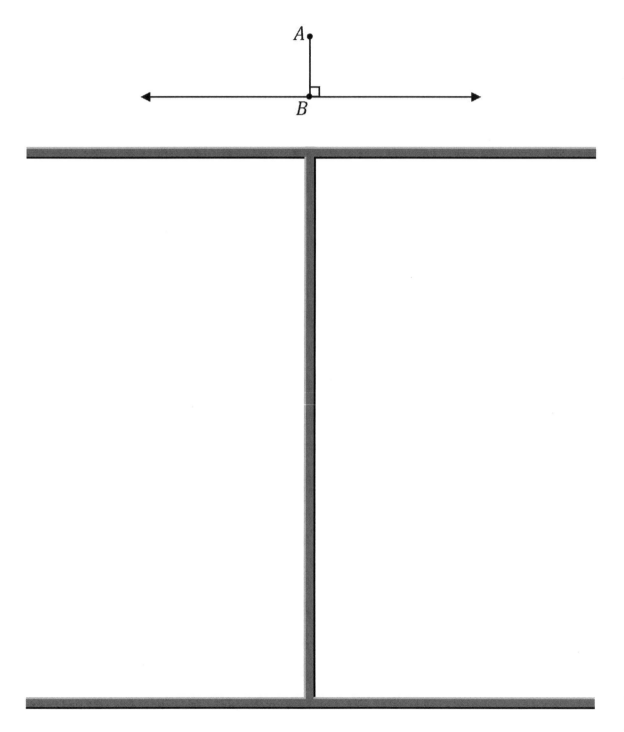

Proof #12. As illustrated below, point C lies on the perpendicular bisector of line segment $\overline{AB}$. Prove that point C is equidistant from points A and B.

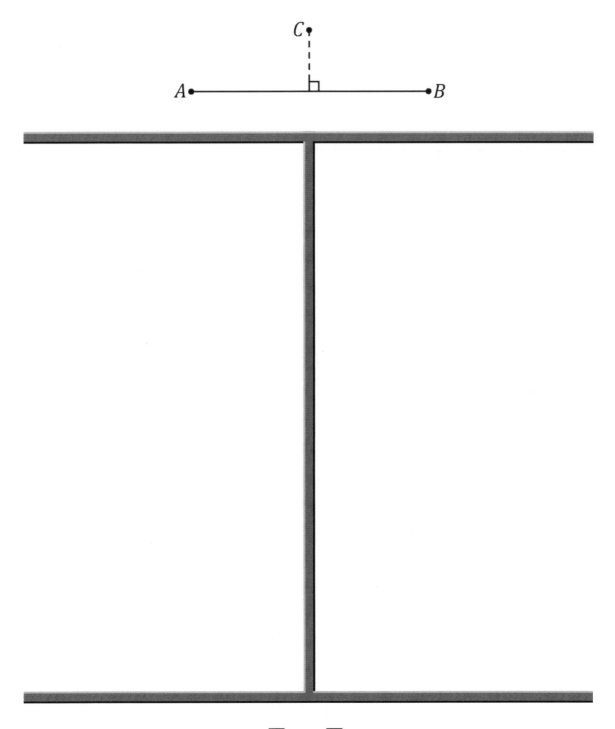

Proof #13. Angle $\angle ADB$ shown below is a right angle. Show that $AB > AD$ and $BC > CD$, and use these inequalities to prove the triangle inequality $AB + BC > AC$.

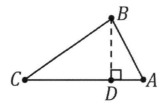

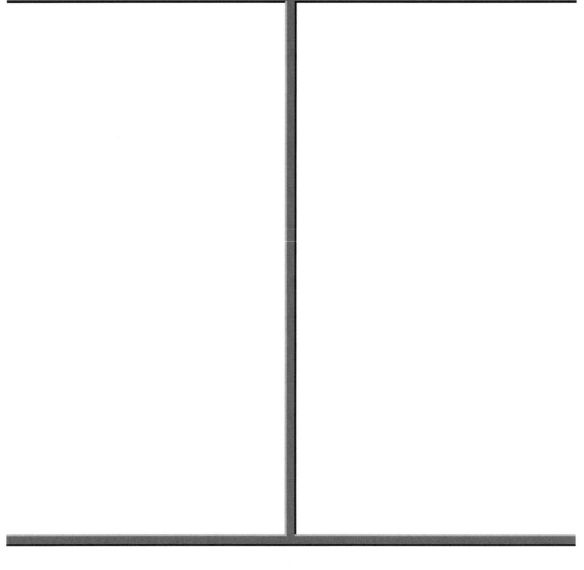

Proof #14. A triangle has edge lengths AB, BC, and AC. Regardless of which side is longest or shortest, prove that $AB > |BC - AC|$ (where this subtraction is enclosed in absolute values).

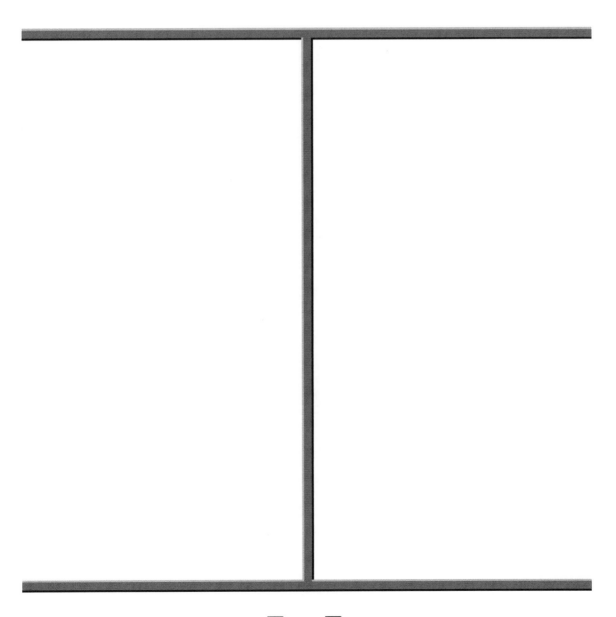

Proof #15. A monkey has two straight sticks. One stick is 6 cm long and the other is 8 cm long. The monkey wishes to combine these two sticks with a third straight stick to form a triangle. Prove that the third stick must be between 2 cm and 14 cm long. Draw pictures to illustrate what these limits of 2 cm and 14 cm represent.

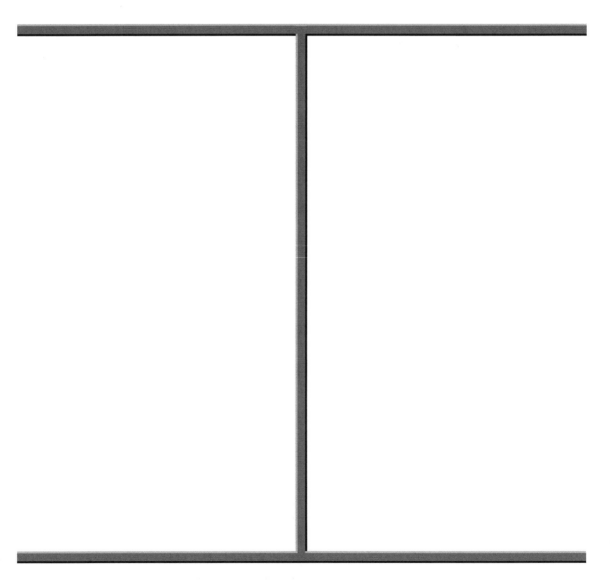

Proof #16. Prove that the edges of a 30° right triangle come in the ratio $1: \sqrt{3}: 2$.

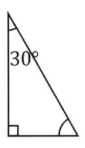

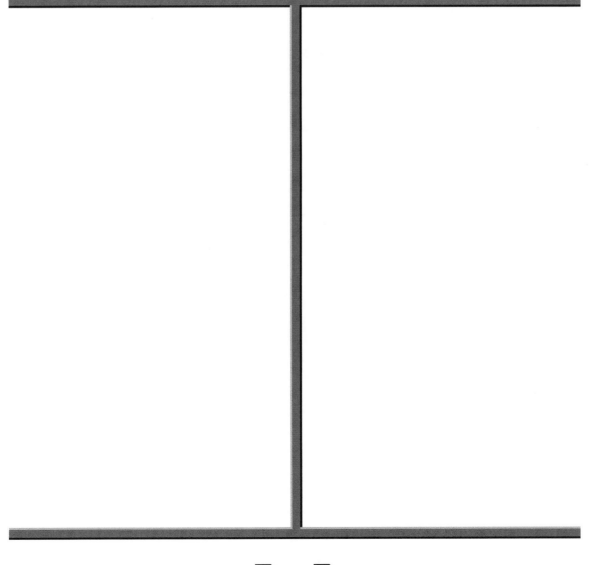

Proof #17. The equilateral triangle shown below has edge length L. Prove that its area is equal to $\frac{L^2\sqrt{3}}{4}$.

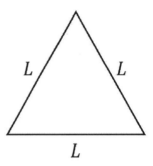

Proof #18. In the diagram below, line segments $\overline{AC}$ and $\overline{DE}$ are parallel. Prove that triangles $\triangle ABC$ and $\triangle DBE$ are similar.

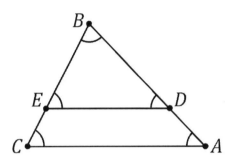

Proof #19. In the diagram below, line segment $\overline{DE}$ is a midsegment, which means that point D bisects $\overline{AB}$ and that point E bisects $\overline{BC}$. Prove that line segments $\overline{AC}$ and $\overline{DE}$ are parallel, and prove that $DE = \frac{1}{2}AC$. This is known as the midsegment theorem. To aid in your proof, line $\overline{DE}$ has been extended such that $\overline{DF} \cong \overline{DE}$.

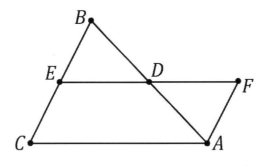

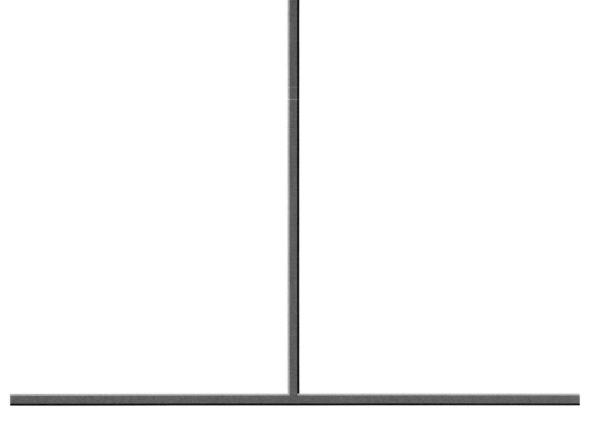

Proof #20. In the diagram below, points D, E, and F are midpoints of their respective sides. Prove that triangles $\triangle BDE$ and $\triangle DAF$ are congruent.

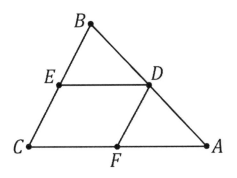

Proof #21. In the diagram below, points D and E are midpoints of $\overline{AB}$ and $\overline{BC}$. Prove that triangles ΔDEF and ΔCAF are similar, and that the length of each edge of ΔCAF is twice as long as the corresponding edge of ΔDEF. (Point F is called the centroid.)

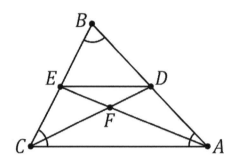

Proof #22. In the diagram below, point F is the centroid (where the medians intersect) of equilateral triangle $\triangle ABC$ and line segment $\overline{DE}$ is parallel to the base. Prove that triangle $\triangle ABC$ can be divided into 9 congruent triangles as illustrated below.

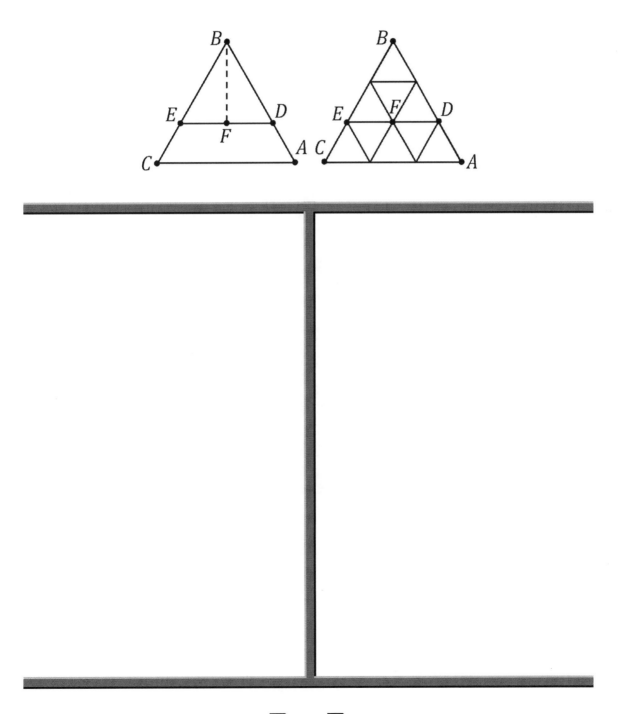

Proof #23. The diagram below shows an equilateral triangle cut into two pieces. Line segments $\overline{AC}$ and $\overline{DE}$ are parallel and point F is the centroid (where the medians intersect). Prove that the ratio of the areas of the bottom piece to the top piece equals 5:4, and offer a conceptual explanation for why the two masses aren't equal (even if the triangle has uniform thickness and density).

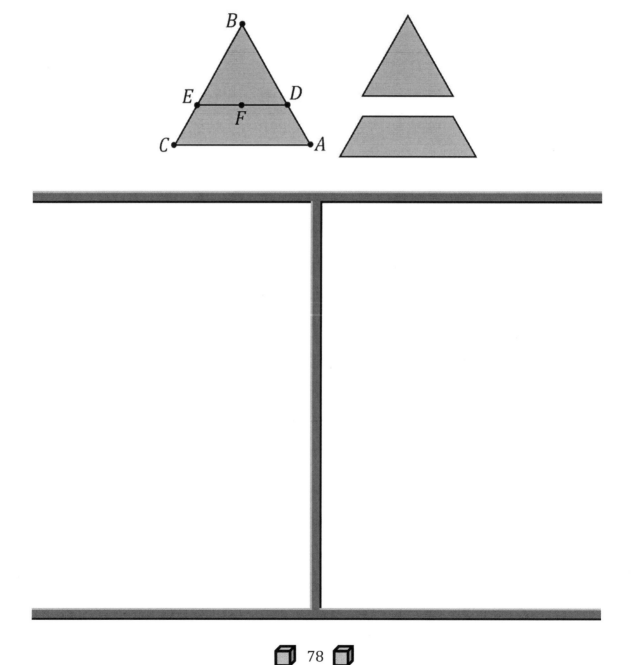

Proof #24. Prove that the midpoint of the hypotenuse of a right triangle is equidistant from all three vertices.

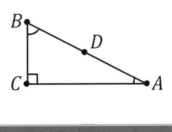

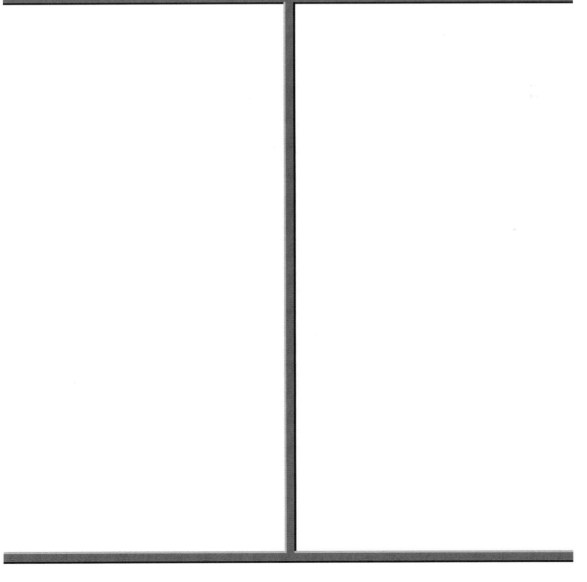

Proof #25. In the diagram below, $\overline{LE} \perp \overline{AB}$, $\overline{EJ} \perp \overline{AC}$, $\angle 1 \cong \angle 3$, and $\angle EDF \cong \angle EFD$. Without making any other assumptions, prove that $m\angle 2 = 2\,m\angle EDF$.

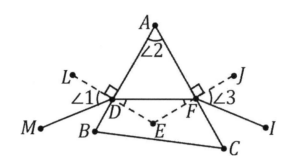

Proof #26. This diagram is the same as for Proof 25, except that line segments $\overline{MD}$ and $\overline{FI}$ have each been extended to form angle $\angle KGI$. Without making any other assumptions beyond those of Proof 25, prove that $m\angle KGI = 2(m\angle 1 - m\angle EDF)$.

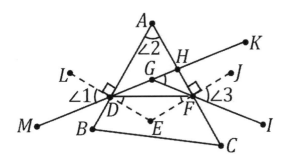

Proof #27. In the diagram below, $\angle ABC$ and $\angle ADE$ are right angles. Prove that $\triangle ABC \sim \triangle CDE$.

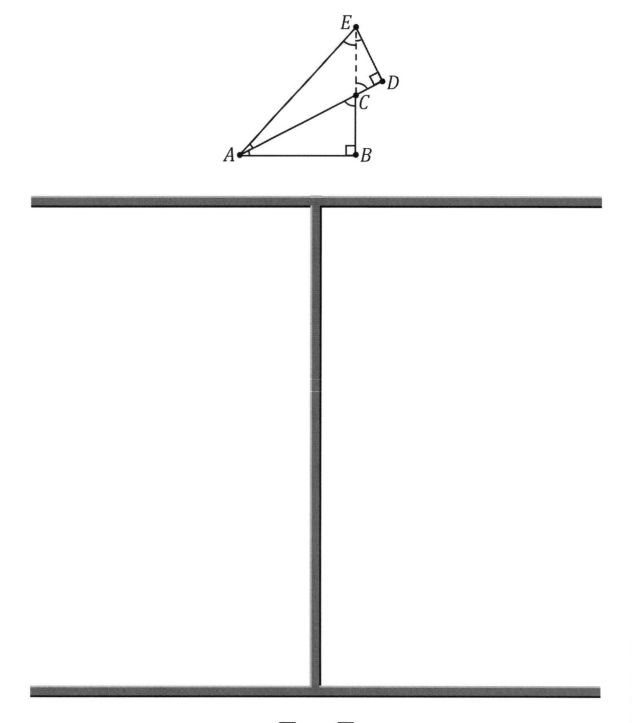

Proof #28. The diagram below consists of one square with edge length c inscribed in a larger square with edge length $a + b$. Use this diagram to prove that $a^2 + b^2 = c^2$, which is the Pythagorean theorem for each of the four right triangles.

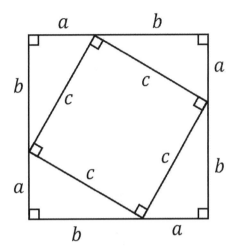

Proof #29. The diagram below consists of one square with edge length $b - a$ inside of a larger square with edge length c. Use this diagram to prove that $a^2 + b^2 = c^2$, which is the Pythagorean theorem for each of the four right triangles.

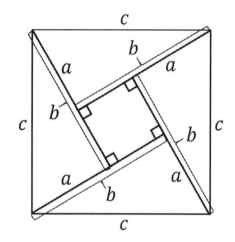

Proof #30. The diagram below consists of a large right triangle that is divided into two smaller right triangles. Use this diagram to prove the Pythagorean theorem for one of the right triangles.

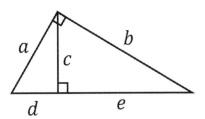

Proof #31. Prove that the area of the trapezoid shown below equals $\left(\frac{a+b}{2}\right) h$.

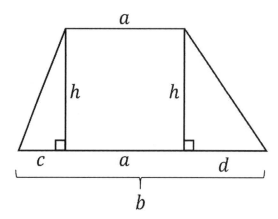

Proof #32. Prove that the area of the parallelogram shown below equals *bh*.

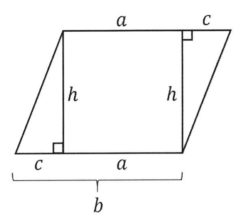

Proof #33. Prove that the diagonals of a parallelogram bisect each other's lengths.

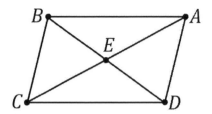

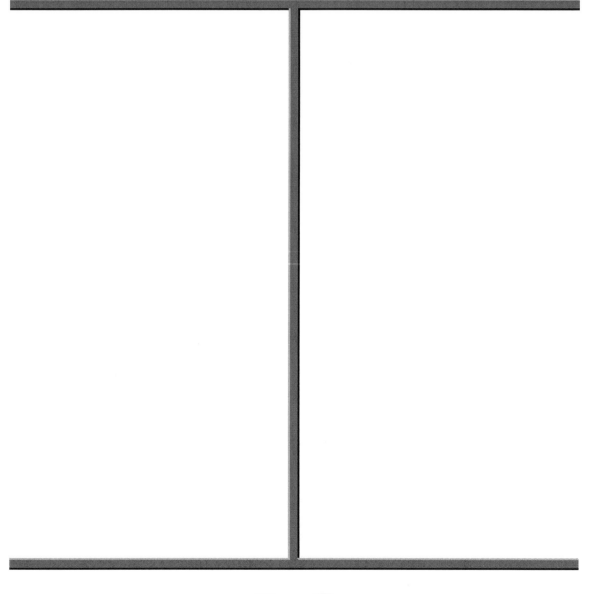

Proof #34. Prove that the diagonals of a rhombus are perpendicular to each other.

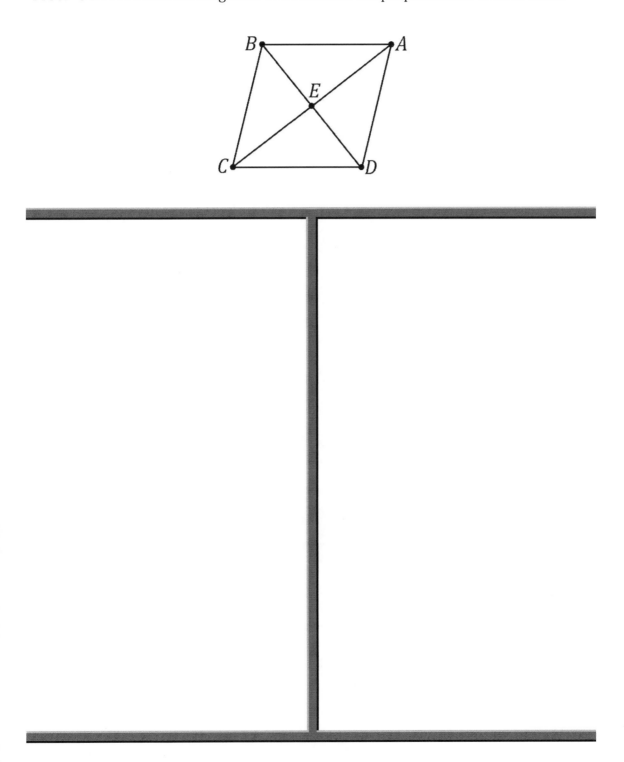

Proof #35. Prove that angles $\angle BAE$ and $\angle DAE$ are congruent for the rhombus below.

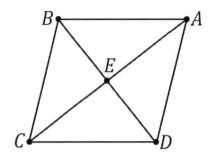

Proof #36. For the kite illustrated below, $\overline{AB}$ is congruent with $\overline{BC}$ and $\overline{AD}$ is congruent with $\overline{CD}$. (Note that the kite is **not** a parallelogram.) Prove that the diagonals of the kite are perpendicular to each other.

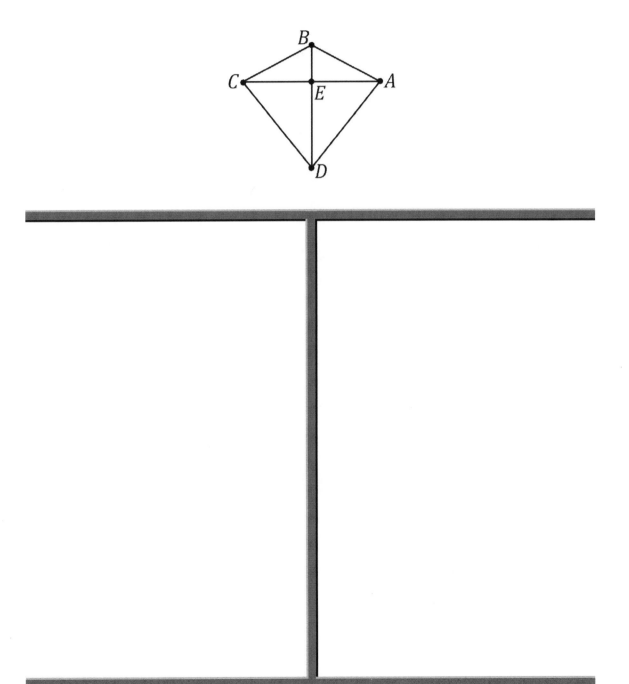

Proof #37. Four identical rods of length L are joined together in the shape of a square with hinges at the vertices, as shown below on the left. Vertices B and D are pushed together, causing the square to turn into the rhombus shown below on the right. In the rhombus, $m\angle B'A'D' = 60°$. Prove that the ratio of the area of the rhombus to the area of the square is $\sqrt{3}: 2$.

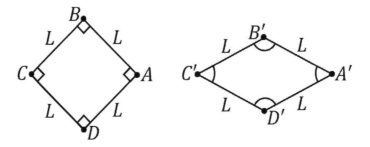

Proof #38. Prove that the area of a regular hexagon with edge length L equals $\frac{3L^2\sqrt{3}}{2}$.

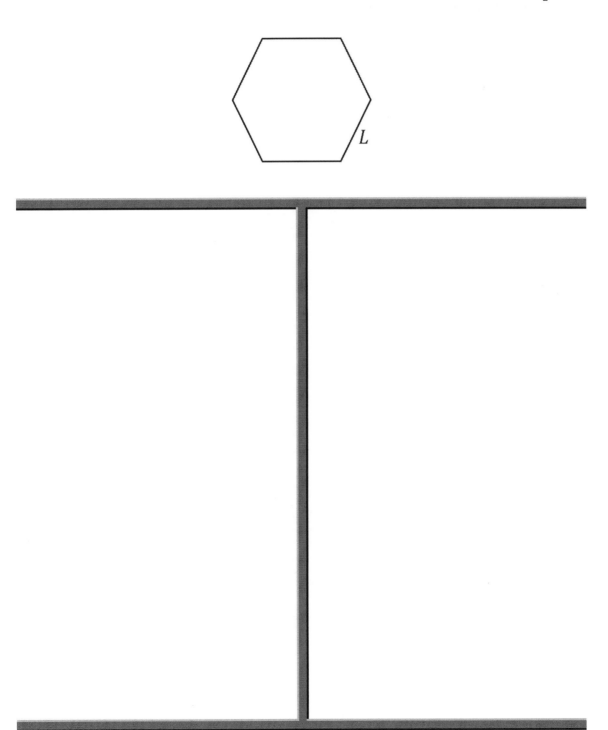

Proof #39. Use the diagram below to prove that the area of a regular octagon with edge length L equals $2L^2\left(1 + \sqrt{2}\right)$.

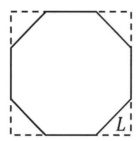

Proof #40. Prove that the arc length of a circular arc equals $s = R\,(m\angle\theta)$, provided that the measured central angle $(m\angle\theta)$ is expressed in radians.

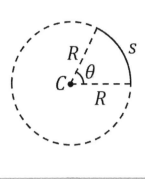

Proof #41. Point C lies at the center of the circle below. The diagram on the right is a magnified version of the triangles (which adds two line segments and labels more angles). Prove that $m\angle\beta = m\angle\alpha + m\angle\sigma$, $m\angle\delta = m\angle\omega + m\angle\mu$, and $\angle\omega \cong \angle\sigma$.

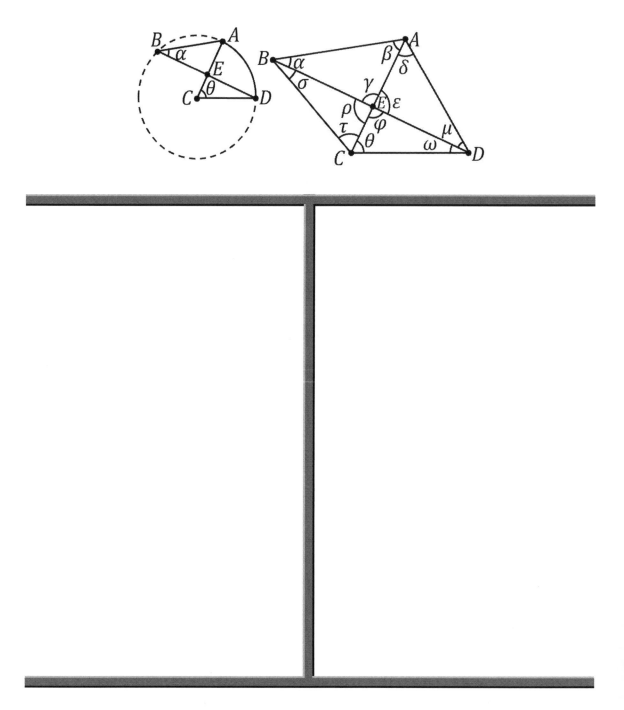

Proof #42. These are the same diagrams as Proof 41. Prove that $m\angle\alpha + m\angle\delta = 90°$.

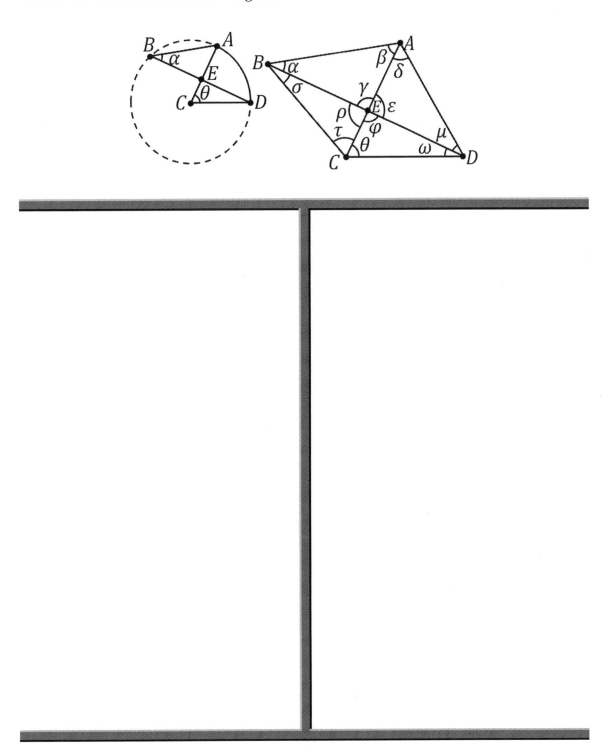

Proof #43. These are the same diagrams as Proofs 41-42. Prove that $m\angle\alpha = \frac{m\angle\theta}{2}$.

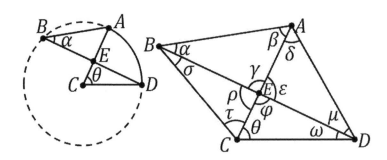

Proof #44. In the diagram below, $\overline{BD}$ is a diameter and point C lies at the center of the circle. Prove that $m\angle\alpha = \frac{m\angle\theta}{2}$. (Don't use the result of Proof 43.)

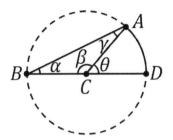

Proof #45. In the diagram below, $\overline{BD}$ is a diameter and point C lies at the center of the circle. Prove Thales's theorem for triangle ΔBAD, which states that if a triangle is inscribed in a circle such that one side of the triangle is a diameter, the angle opposite to the diameter is a right angle.

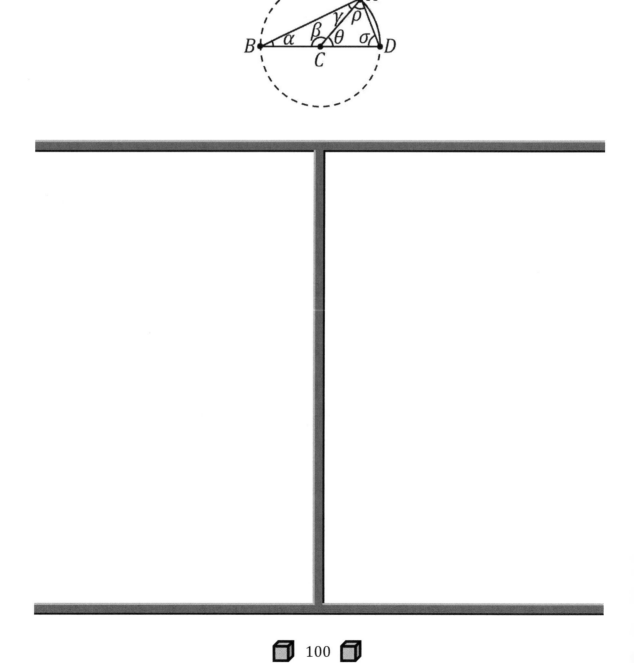

Proof #46. Point C lies at the center of the circle below. Angle $\angle \alpha$ is the angle between chord $\overline{AB}$ and the line that is tangent to the circle at point A. Prove that $m\angle \alpha = \frac{m\angle \theta}{2}$.

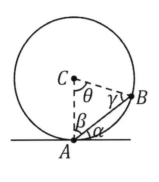

Proof #47. In the diagram below, $\overline{JN}$ and $\overline{KM}$ are intersecting chords. The point of intersection (L) doesn't lie at the center of the circle. None of the sides of quadrilateral $JKNM$ are parallel. Prove that triangles ΔJKL and ΔLMN are similar.

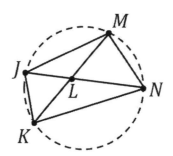

Proof #48. This is the same diagram as Proof 47. Prove that $JL \cdot LN = KL \cdot LM$.

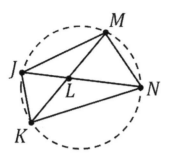

Proof #49. This is the same diagram as Proofs 47-48, except that the diagram on the right adds line segment $\overline{PQ}$ which passes through L as well as the center (C) of the circle. Prove that $JL \cdot LN = KL \cdot LM = R^2 - LC^2$ (where R is the radius of the circle).

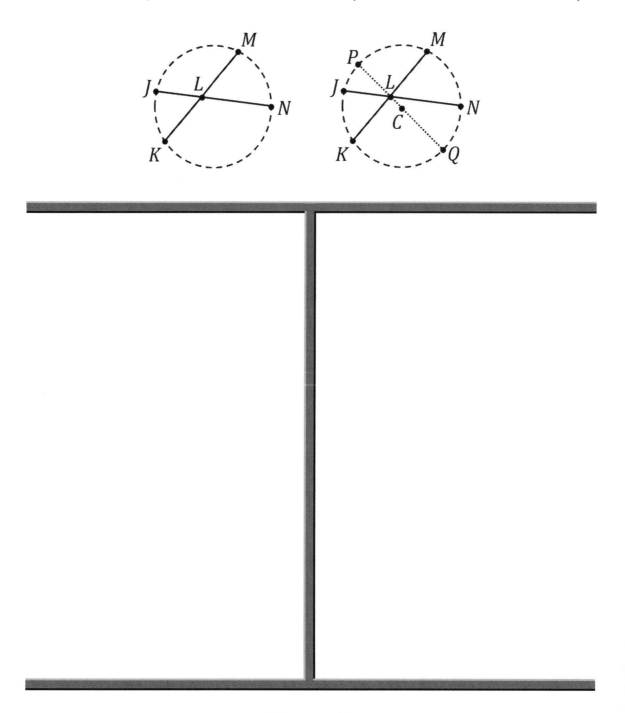

Proof #50. Point C lies at the center of the circle below. $\overline{AD}$ and $\overline{BE}$ are intersecting chords. Prove that $m\angle\alpha = \frac{m\angle\theta + m\angle\varphi}{2}$, where $\angle\theta$ and $\angle\varphi$ are the central angles corresponding to the arcs between B and D and between A and E.

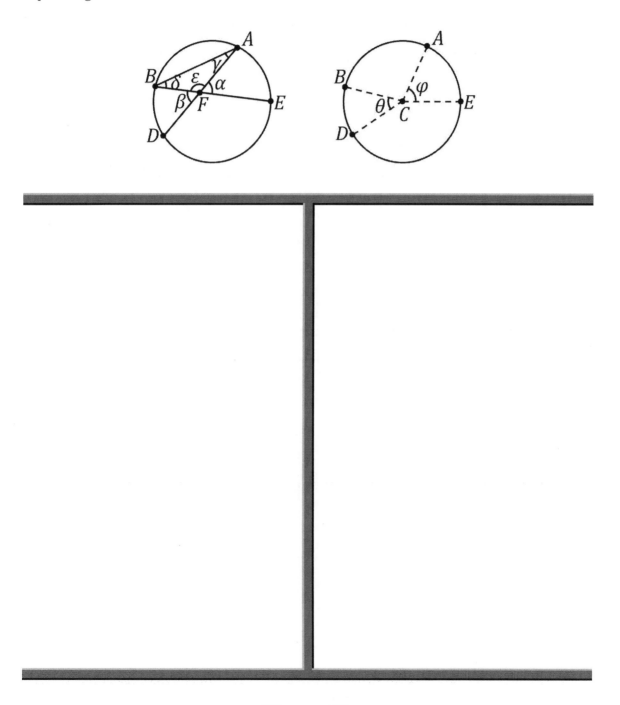

Proof #51. In the diagram below, $\overline{JL}$ and $\overline{KL}$ are intersecting secants. Prove that triangles ΔJLN and ΔKLM are similar.

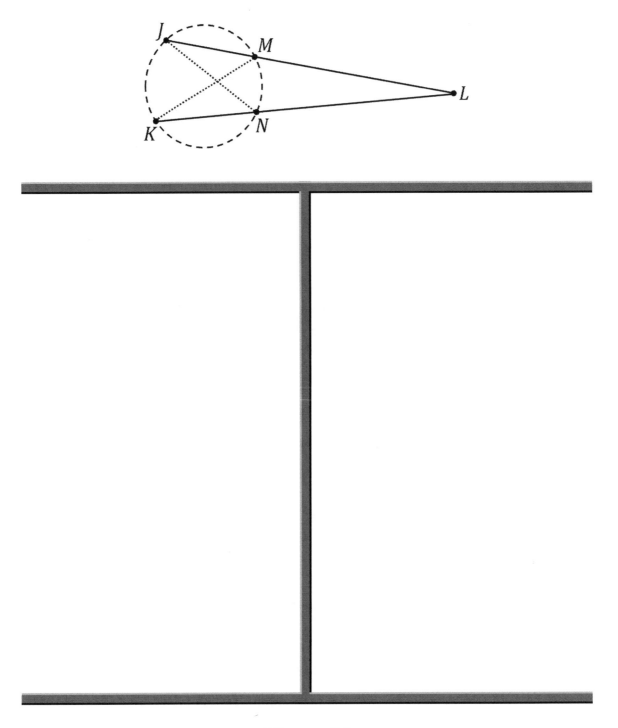

Proof #52. This is the same diagram as Proof 51. Prove that $LN \cdot LK = LM \cdot LJ$.

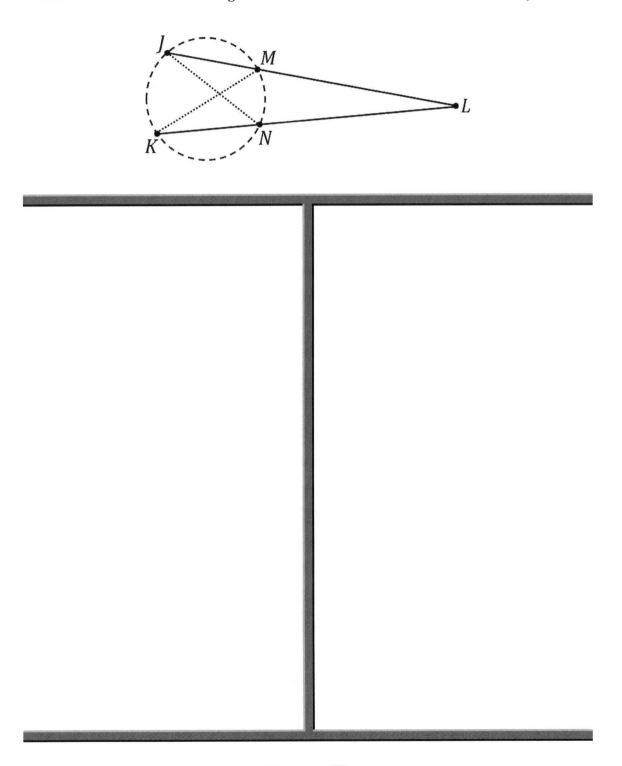

Proof #53. This is the same diagram as Proofs 51-52, except that this diagram adds secant $\overline{LP}$ which passes through the center (C) of the circle. Prove that $LN \cdot LK = LM \cdot LJ = LC^2 - R^2$ (where R is the radius of the circle).

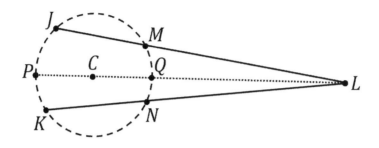

Proof #54. Point C lies at the center of the circle below. $\overline{JL}$ and $\overline{KL}$ are intersecting secants. Prove that $m\angle\alpha = \frac{m\angle\theta - m\angle\varphi}{2}$, where $\angle\theta$ and $\angle\varphi$ are the central angles corresponding to the arcs between J and K and between M and N.

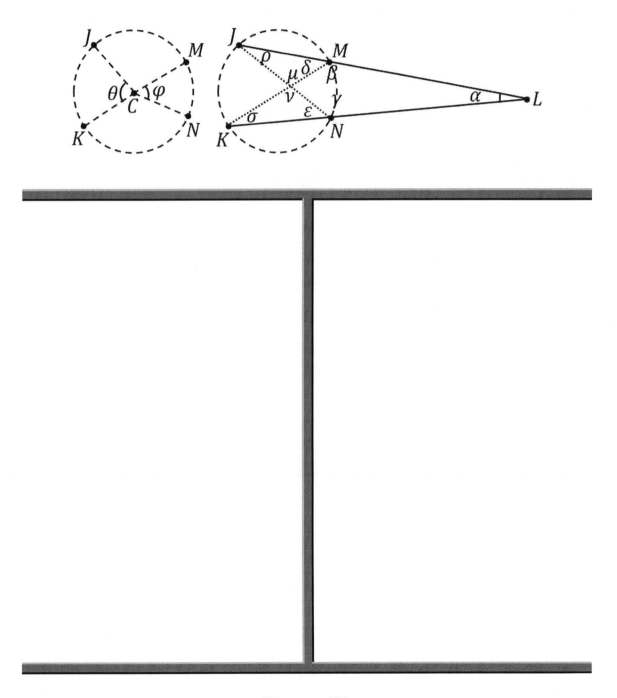

Proof #55. In the diagram below, tangent $\overline{JL}$ and secant $\overline{KL}$ intersect at point L. Prove that triangles $\triangle JLN$ and $\triangle KLJ$ are similar.

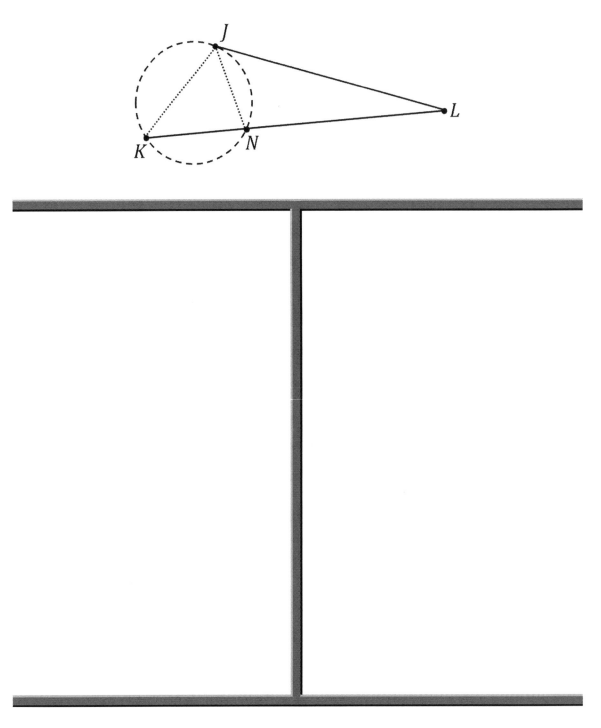

Proof #56. This is the same diagram as Proof 55. Prove that $LN \cdot LK = LJ^2$.

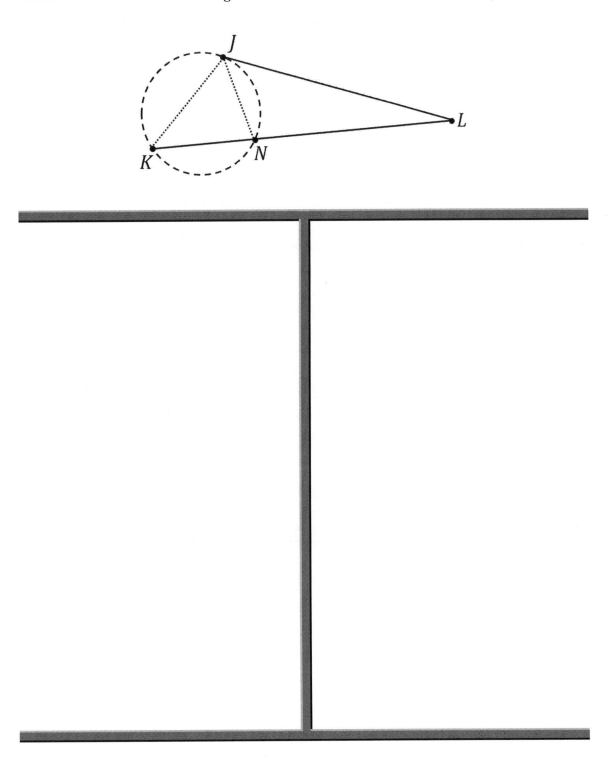

Proof #57. In the diagram below, a square is circumscribed about a circle (which means that the circle is inscribed in the square). The radius of the circle is R and the edge length of the square is L. Prove that $L = 2R$.

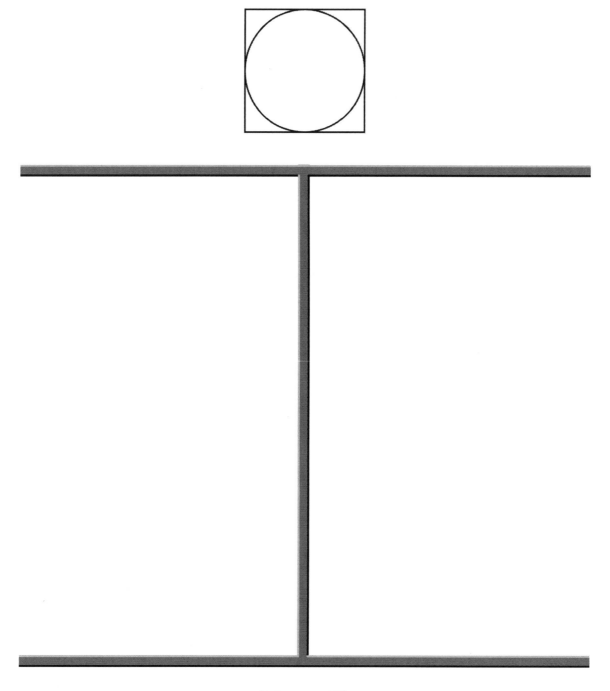

Proof #58. In the diagram below, a square is inscribed in a circle (which means that the circle is circumscribed about the square). The radius of the circle is R and the edge length of the square is L. Prove that $L = R\sqrt{2}$.

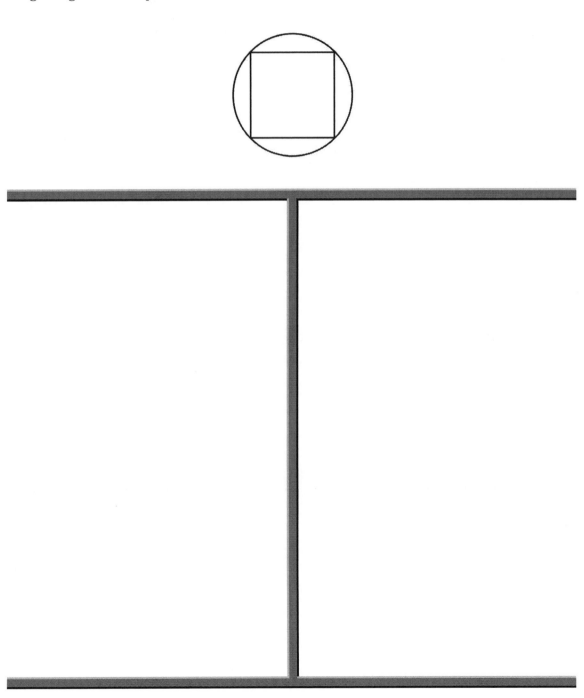

Proof #59. In the diagram below, a regular hexagon is circumscribed about a circle (which means that the circle is inscribed in the hexagon). The radius of the circle is R and the edge length of the hexagon is L. Prove that $L = \frac{2R\sqrt{3}}{3}$.

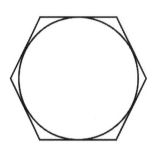

Proof #60. In the diagram below, a regular hexagon is inscribed in a circle (which means that the circle is circumscribed about the hexagon). The radius of the circle is R and the edge length of the hexagon is L. Prove that $L = R$.

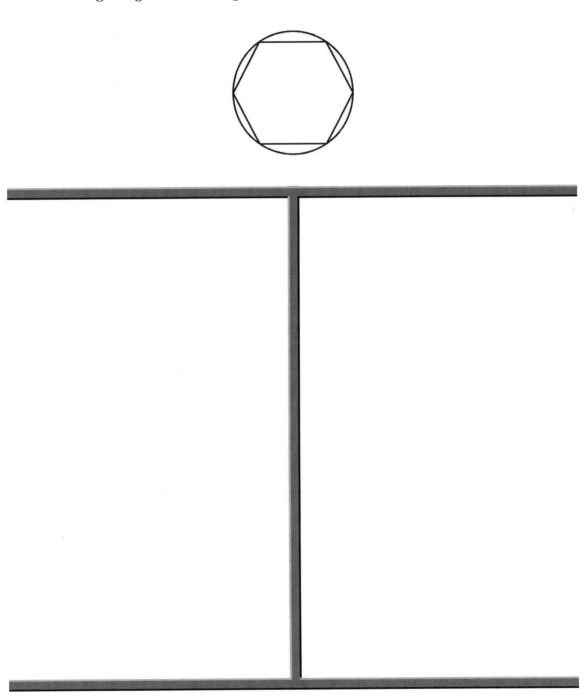

Proof #61. In the diagram below, an equilateral triangle is circumscribed about a circle (which means that the circle is inscribed in the triangle). The radius of the circle is R and the edge length of the triangle is L. Prove that $L = 2R\sqrt{3}$.

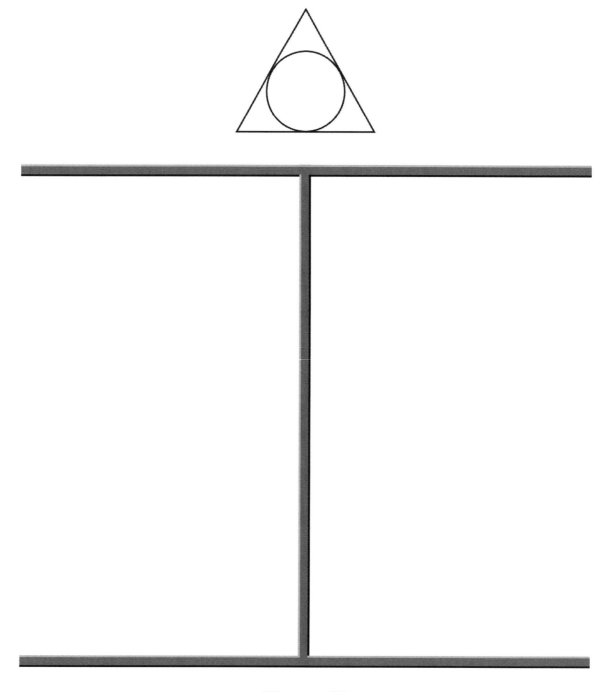

Proof #62. In the diagram below, an equilateral triangle is inscribed in a circle (which means that the circle is circumscribed about the triangle). The radius of the circle is R and the edge length of the triangle is L. Prove that $L = R\sqrt{3}$.

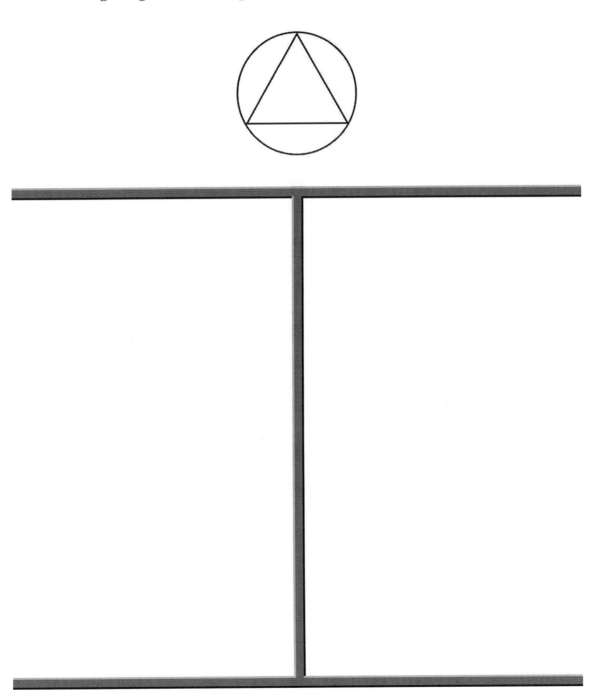

Proof #63. In the diagram below, two congruent circles with radius R are centered about C and D, and intersect at A and B such that $AB = R$. Prove that $CD = R\sqrt{3}$.

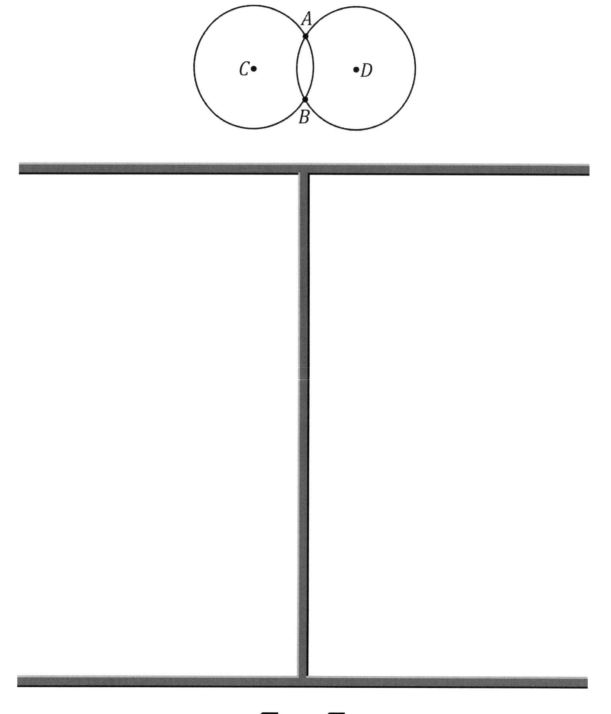

Proof #64. In the diagram below, three circles touch at their rightmost points. The middle circle has twice the radius of the small circle and the large circle has triple the radius of the small circle. Prove that the area of the shaded region is twice the area of the unshaded region.

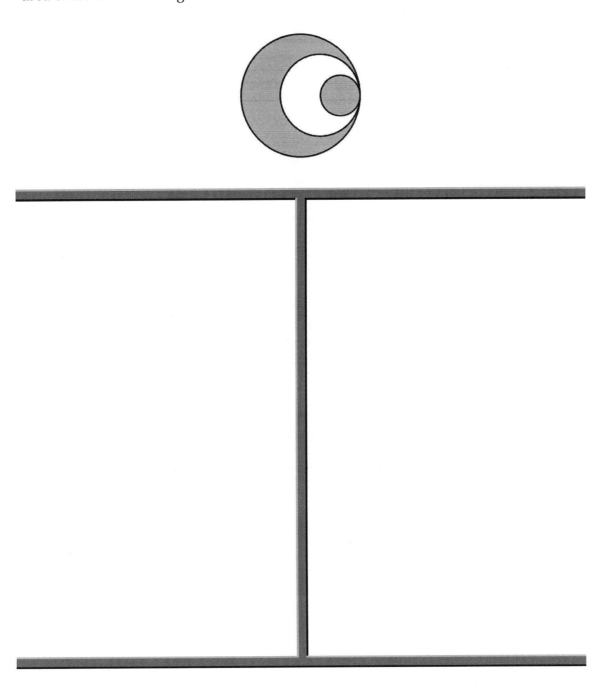

Hint for Proof #1. The logic behind this proof is almost identical to Example 1, but you will need to adapt the notation and language to angles instead of line segments.

Hint for Proof #2. You may apply the angle sum theorem for triangles to this proof.

Hint for Proof #3. Apply the parallel postulate like we did in Example 3.

Hint for Proof #4. Two sides of the triangle are transversals. Look for alternate interior angles.

Hint for Proof #5. Draw and label a point near the center of the polygon shown, and draw lines to connect this point to each vertex. Use the newly formed triangles to relate the central angles to the interior angles.

Hint for Proof #6. Use the result of Proof 5.

Hint for Proof #7. Apply the result of Proof 5 to a regular polygon.

Hint for Proof #8. Apply the result of Proof 6 to a regular polygon.

Hint for Proof #9. First prove that triangles ΔBAD and ΔFAC are similar. Next prove that triangles ΔBDE and ΔCFE are similar. The sides of similar triangles come in the same proportions. Use this to establish the relevant ratio.

Hint for Proof #10. First prove that the two smaller triangles are congruent, and then apply the CPCTC.

Hint for Proof #11. Draw another line segment connecting point A to the line, which isn't perpendicular to the line. Apply the Pythagorean theorem.

Hint for Proof #12. Form two triangles. Prove that these triangles are congruent, and then apply the CPCTC.

Hint for Proof #13. Use the result of Proof 11.

Hint for Proof #14. Apply the triangle inequality. Note that the triangle inequality may be written three different ways for any given triangle (Chapter 3).

Hint for Proof #15. Use the results of Proofs 13-14.

Hint for Proof #16. This is very similar to Example 4. Put two of these triangles together to form an equilateral triangle in order to show that the hypotenuse is twice as long as the side opposite to the 30° angle.

Hint for Proof #17. Cut the equilateral triangle in half vertically and use the results of Proof 16.

Hint for Proof #18. Look for transversals and corresponding angles.

Hint for Proof #19. Prove that the smaller triangles are congruent and that $ACEF$ is a parallelogram.

Hint for Proof #20. Use the results of Proofs 18-19.

Hint for Proof #21. Use the results of Proofs 18-20.

Hint for Proof #22. Use the results of Proofs 19-21 to show that $\overline{DE}$, $\overline{GI}$, and $\overline{HJ}$ are parallel to one side of triangle $\triangle ABC$. Show that the small triangles are equiangular and that their edge lengths and heights are one-third of the edge length and height of $\triangle ABC$.

Hint for Proof #23. Use the result of Proof 22.

Hint for Proof #24. Draw a line parallel to the base passing through point D. Show that this line is parallel to the bottom side. Look for congruent triangles.

Hint for Proof #25. Use triangle $\triangle DEF$ and quadrilateral $ADEF$.

Hint for Proof #26. Use triangle $\triangle DGF$.

Hint for Proof #27. Prove that two angles are congruent.

Hint for Proof #28. Find the area of the large square two different ways.

Hint for Proof #29. Find the area of the large square two different ways.

Hint for Proof #30. First show that the two small triangles and the large triangle are all similar. Use the property of similar triangles that corresponding sides come in the same proportions to write equations involving ratios of the sides. Cross multiply and use algebra to form the Pythagorean theorem.

Hint for Proof #31. The area of a region equals the sum of the areas of its non-overlapping parts.

Hint for Proof #32. The area of a region equals the sum of the areas of its non-overlapping parts.

Hint for Proof #33. Identify congruent triangles.

Hint for Proof #34. Identify congruent triangles. What is the definition of a rhombus?

Hint for Proof #35. Identify congruent triangles. What is the definition of a rhombus?

Hint for Proof #36. Identify congruent triangles.

Hint for Proof #37. Note that the height of the rhombus isn't given (only an edge and an interior angle are given), so it won't help to use the formula for the area of a parallelogram unless you first determine the height. Rather than find the height, divide the rhombus into 4 congruent triangles and find the area of each triangle.

Hint for Proof #38. Divide the hexagon into 6 triangles. Show that they are equilateral.

Hint for Proof #39. First prove that the four triangles are 45° right triangles with edge length $\frac{L}{\sqrt{2}}$, such that the square has edge length $L(1 + \sqrt{2})$. Subtract the area of the triangles from the area of the square.

Hint for Proof #40. How many radians correspond to one full circle? Setup a proportion, comparing the central angle and arc length of a circular arc to the central angle and circumference of one full circle.

Hint for Proof #41. Any line segment connecting the center of the circle to its edge is a radius. Identify the radii in the diagram on the right. This will help you to identify isosceles triangles. Use the result of Proof 10.

Hint for Proof #42. Use the angle sum theorem for triangles and the results of Proof 41.

Hint for Proof #43. Use the angle sum theorem for triangles and the results of Proofs 41-42.

Hint for Proof #44. Any line segment connecting the center of the circle to its edge is a radius. Use the result of Proof 10 and the angle sum theorem for triangles.

Hint for Proof #45. Any line segment connecting the center of the circle to its edge is a radius. Use the result of Proof 10 and the angle sum theorem for triangles.

Hint for Proof #46. Any line segment connecting the center of the circle to its edge is a radius. Use the result of Proof 10 and the angle sum theorem for triangles.

Hint for Proof #47. Use the result of Proof 43.

Hint for Proof #48. Use the result of Proof 47.

Hint for Proof #49. Use the result of Proof 48. Also apply this to diameter $\overline{PQ}$. Note that CP and CQ are each equal to a radius. Rewrite distances LP and LQ in terms of CP and CQ.

Hint for Proof #50. Use the angle sum theorem for triangles and the result of Proof 43.

Hint for Proof #51. Use the result of Proof 43.

Hint for Proof #52. Use the result of Proof 51.

Hint for Proof #53. Use the result of Proof 52. Also apply this to secant $\overline{LP}$. Note that CP and CQ are each equal to a radius. Rewrite distances LP and LQ in terms of CP and CQ.

Hint for Proof #54. Use the angle sum theorem for triangles and the result of Proof 43.

Hint for Proof #55. Use the result of Proof 46 to find the angle between a chord and a tangent. Also use the result of Proof 43.

Hint for Proof #56. Use the result of Proof 55.

Hint for Proof #57. Draw a horizontal (or vertical) diameter.

Hint for Proof #58. Draw a diagonal line joining two corners of the square. Also draw horizontal and vertical diameters. It may help to review Proof 19.

Hint for Proof #59. Divide the hexagon into 6 equilateral triangles as we did in Proof 38. It may help to review Proofs 16-17.

Hint for Proof #60. Divide the hexagon into 6 equilateral triangles as we did in Proofs 38 and 59.

Hint for Proof #61. Divide the triangle into 4 equilateral triangles. Use the result of Proofs 18-21. It may help to review Proofs 16-17. **Suggestion**: Do Proof 62 first.

Hint for Proof #62. Draw the three medians which intersect at the centroid. Use the result of Proofs 18-21. It may help to review Proofs 16-17.

Hint for Proof #63. Connect the points and look for special triangles. It may help to review Proofs 16-17.

Hint for Proof #64. Let the radius of the small circle be R. Express the area of each individual circle in terms of R. Combine these areas together to determine the area of the shaded and unshaded regions.

Solution to Proof #1.

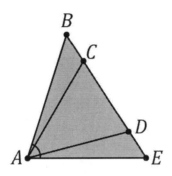

❶ $\angle BAC \cong \angle DAE$.	❶ Given.
❷ $m\angle BAC = m\angle DAE$.	❷ Def. of congr. applied to Step 1.
❸ $m\angle BAC + m\angle CAD$ $= m\angle DAE + m\angle CAD$.	❸ Add $m\angle CAD$ to both sides of Step 2.
❹ $m\angle BAC + m\angle CAD = m\angle BAD$.	❹ Prop. of addition.
❺ $m\angle DAE + m\angle CAD = m\angle CAE$.	❺ Prop. of addition.
❻ $m\angle BAD = m\angle CAE$.	❻ Sub. Steps 4-5 into Step 3.
❼ $\angle BAD \cong \angle CAE$. ∎	❼ Def. of congr. applied to Step 6. ∎

Note:

- This is like Example 1, except that these are angles instead of line segments.

Solution to Proof #2.

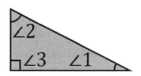

❶ $m\angle 3 = 90°$.

❷ $m\angle 1 + m\angle 2 + m\angle 3 = 180°$.

❸ $m\angle 1 + m\angle 2 + 90° = 180°$.

❹ $m\angle 1 + m\angle 2 = 90°$.

❺ $\angle 1$ and $\angle 2$ are complements. ■

❶ Def. of right triangle.

❷ Angle sum thm. for a triangle.

❸ Sub. Step 1 into Step 2.

❹ Subtract 90° from both sides of Step 3.

❺ Def. of compl. applied to Step 4. ■

Solution to Proof #3.

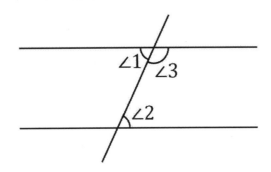

❶ Top line ∥ bottom line.	❶ Given.
❷ $m\angle2 + m\angle3 = 180°$.	❷ The parallel postulate. (If this were not true, the top and bottom lines would intersect.)
❸ $m\angle1 + m\angle3 = 180°$.	❸ Suppl. angles.
❹ $m\angle2 + m\angle3 = m\angle1 + m\angle3$.	❹ Set Eq.'s 2 and 3 equal.
❺ $m\angle2 = m\angle1$.	❺ Subtract $m\angle3$ from both sides of Step 4.
❻ $\angle2 \cong \angle1$. ∎	❻ Def. of congr. applied to Step 5. ∎

Solution to Proof #4.

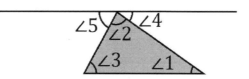

❶ Top line ∥ base of triangle.	❶ Given.
❷ The top sides of the triangle are transversals.	❷ Def. of transversal.
❸ ∠3 ≅ ∠5.	❸ Alt. int. angles.
❹ ∠1 ≅ ∠4.	❹ Alt. int. angles.
❺ $m\angle 5 + m\angle 2 + m\angle 4 = 180°$.	❺ These angles form a straight line. ∠5 and ∠(2 + 4) are supplements.
❻ $m\angle 3 + m\angle 2 + m\angle 1 = 180°$. ∎	❻ Sub. Steps 3-4 into Step 5. ∎

Solution to Proof #5.

❶ $m\angle 1 + m\angle 2 + m\angle 3 + \cdots + m\angle N$
$= 360°.$

❷ $m\angle a + m\angle b + m\angle 1 = 180°$
$m\angle c + m\angle d + m\angle 2 = 180°$
$m\angle e + m\angle f + m\angle 3 = 180°$
and so on.

❸ $m\angle a + m\angle b = 180° - m\angle 1$
$m\angle c + m\angle d = 180° - m\angle 2$
$m\angle e + m\angle f = 180° - m\angle 3$
and so on.

❹ $m\angle a + m\angle b + m\angle c + m\angle d$
$+ m\angle e + m\angle f + \cdots$
$= 180° - m\angle 1 + 180° - m\angle 2$
$+180° - m\angle 3 + \cdots.$

❺ $m\angle a + m\angle b + m\angle c + m\angle d$
$+ m\angle e + m\angle f + \cdots$
$= N(180°) - 360°.$

❻ $(N - 2)180° = N(180°) - 360°.$

❼ $m\angle a + m\angle b + m\angle c + m\angle d$
$+ m\angle e + m\angle f + \cdots$
$= (N - 2)180°.$ ∎

❶ Central angles forming a full circle add up to 360°.

❷ Angle sum thm. for triangles.

❸ Subtract the central angle from each eq. in Step 2.

❹ Add the eq.'s in Step 3. The sum of the left-hand sides equals the sum of the right-hand sides.

❺ Sub. Step 1 into Step 4. The angular meas. of central angles forming a full circle sum to 360°. There are N terms equal to 180°.

❻ Distributive prop. of algebra.

❼ Sub. Step 6 into Step 5. ∎
Note that $\angle(b + c)$, $\angle(d + e)$, etc. are the interior angles.

See the notes on the following page.

Notes for Proof 5:

- The symbol $\cdots$ means "and so on." Although a pentagon is drawn, we want to prove our equation for an N-sided polygon (not just for a 5-sided polygon).
- $\angle 1$, $\angle 2$, $\angle 3$, etc. are central angles. Their angular measures add up to $360°$.
- We divided the polygon up into N triangles. We applied the angle sum theorem to each triangle in Step 2.
- The right-hand side of Step 4 adds $180°$ a total of N times. This is where the term $N(180°)$ comes from.
- On the right-hand side of Step 4, $-m\angle 1 - m\angle 2 - m\angle 3 - \cdots - m\angle N = -360°$ according to Step 1 (if you multiply both sides of Step 1 by minus one).
- The interior angles are $\angle(b+c)$, $\angle(d+e)$, $\angle(f+g)$, and so on, where these angles are formed by combining two adjacent angles together.
- The left-hand side of Step 7 effectively adds the interior angles together. Note that $m\angle b + m\angle c$ is the angular measure of one interior angle, $m\angle d + m\angle e$ is the angular measure of another interior angle, etc.

Notes for Proof 6:

- The symbol $\cdots$ means "and so on."
- Step 1 is equivalent to the last step of Proof 5. Note that in Proof 6 $\angle a$, $\angle b$, $\angle c$, etc. are the interior angles, since we defined these angles different from how we defined the angles in Proof 5. The left-hand sides of Step 1 of Proof 6 and Step 7 of Proof 5 are equivalent: The notation is different because each angle from Proof 6 is split into two separate angles in Proof 5.
- For every interior angle, the corresponding exterior angle is its supplement. We used this in Step 2.
- The left-hand side of Step 4 adds $180°$ a total of N times. This is where the term $N(180°)$ comes from.
- Step 5 applies the distributive property: $(N-2)180° = N(180°) - 360°$.
- In Step 6, after canceling $N(180°)$ on both sides, we multiplied both sides of the equation by minus one (which negates all of the minus signs).

 132

Solution to Proof #6.

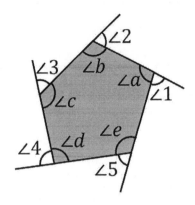

❶ $m\angle a + m\angle b + m\angle c + m\angle d$ $+ \cdots = (N-2)180°$.	❶ We showed this in Proof 5. Still true even though we defined the angles differently here.
❷ $m\angle a + m\angle 1 = 180°$ $m\angle b + m\angle 2 = 180°$ $m\angle c + m\angle 3 = 180°$ and so on.	❷ Suppl. angles.
❸ $m\angle a = 180° - m\angle 1$ $m\angle b = 180° - m\angle 2$ $m\angle c = 180° - m\angle 3$ and so on.	❸ Subtract the exterior angle from each eq. in Step 2.
❹ $180° - m\angle 1 + 180° - m\angle 2$ $180° - m\angle 3 + \cdots = (N-2)180°$.	❹ Sub. Step 3 into Step 1.
❺ $N(180°) - m\angle 1 - m\angle 2 - m\angle 3 \cdots$ $= N(180°) - 360°$.	❺ There are N terms equal to 180°. Apply the distributive property.
❻ $m\angle 1 + m\angle 2 + m\angle 3 + \cdots = 360°$. ∎	❻ Cancel $N(180°)$ and mult. by -1. ∎

See the notes on the previous page.

Solution to Proof #7.

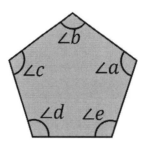

❶ $m\angle a + m\angle b + m\angle c + m\angle d$ $+ \cdots = (N - 2)180°.$	❶ We showed this in Proof 5. See the note below.
❷ $m\angle a = m\angle b = m\angle c = \cdots$	❷ Regular polygons are equiangular.
❸ $m\angle a + m\angle a + m\angle a + m\angle a$ $+ \cdots = (N - 2)180°.$	❸ Sub. Step 2 into Step 1.
❹ $N(m\angle a) = (N - 2)180°.$	❹ The angular measures for N interior angles are added together.
❺ $N(m\angle a) = N(180°) - 360°.$	❺ Distributive prop. of algebra..
❻ $(m\angle a) = 180° - \frac{360°}{N}.$ ∎	❻ Divide each term of Step 5 by N. ∎

Notes:

- Step 1 states that the sum of the angular measures of the interior angles of a polygon is $(N - 2)180°$, which is what we proved in Proof 5. As with Proof 6, in Proof 7 we have defined and labeled the angles differently from Proof 5, but the expression that we have written down in Step 1 is equivalent to Proof 5.

- Step 2 states that the interior angles of a regular polygon are congruent.

- $m\angle a + m\angle a + m\angle a + m\angle a + \cdots = N(m\angle a).$

- $(N - 2)180° = N(180°) - 360°.$

- $\frac{N(m\angle a)}{N} = \frac{N(180°)}{N} - \frac{360°}{N}$ simplifies to $(m\angle a) = 180° - \frac{360°}{N}.$

Solution to Proof #8.

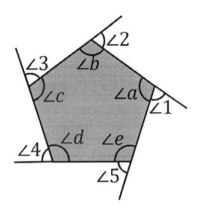

1 $m\angle 1 + m\angle 2 + m\angle 3 + \cdots = 360°$	**1** We showed this in Proof 6.
2 $m\angle a = m\angle b = m\angle c = \cdots$	**2** Regular polygons are equiangular.
3 $m\angle a + m\angle 1 = 180°$ $m\angle b + m\angle 2 = 180°$ $m\angle c + m\angle 3 = 180°$ and so on.	**3** Suppl. angles.
4 $m\angle 1 = m\angle 2 = m\angle 3 = \cdots$	**4** Follows from Steps 2 and 3. See the note below.
5 $m\angle 1 + m\angle 1 + m\angle 1 + \cdots = 360°$.	**5** Sub. Step 4 into Step 1.
6 $N(m\angle 1) = 360°$.	**6** The angular measures for N exterior angles are added together.
7 $m\angle 1 = \dfrac{360°}{N}$. ∎	**7** Divide each term of Step 6 by N. ∎

Note:

- Since the exterior angles are supplements to the interior angles, a regular polygon must have congruent interior angles as well as congruent exterior angles (but the exterior angles generally differ from the interior angles).

Solution to Proof #9.

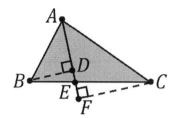

❶ $\angle BAD \cong \angle FAC$ and $\angle ADB \cong \angle AFC$.	❶ Given.
❷ $\triangle BAD \sim \triangle FAC$.	❷ Two angles are congr. in Step 1.
❸ $\angle BDE \cong \angle EFC$.	❸ $\angle BDE$ is suppl. to a right angle. $\angle EFC$ is given to be a right angle.
❹ $\angle BED \cong \angle FEC$.	❹ Vertical angles.
❺ $\triangle BDE \sim \triangle CFE$.	❺ Two angles are congr. in Steps 3-4.
❻ $\frac{AB}{BD} = \frac{AC}{CF}$.	❻ Similarity: $AB : BD : AD = AC : CF : AF$.
❼ $\frac{BD}{BE} = \frac{CF}{CE}$.	❼ Similarity: $BD : DE : BE = CF : FE : CE$.
❽ $\frac{AB}{BE} = \frac{AC}{CE}$.	❽ Mult. Steps 6 and 7.
❾ $\frac{AB}{AC} = \frac{BE}{CE}$. ■	❾ Algebra (see the notes below). ■

Notes:

- $\sim$ represents similarity whereas $\cong$ represents congruence.
- $\left(\frac{AB}{BD}\right)\left(\frac{BD}{BE}\right) = \left(\frac{AC}{CF}\right)\left(\frac{CF}{CE}\right)$ reduces to $\frac{AB}{BE} = \frac{AC}{CE}$ (because BD and CF cancel out).
- $\frac{AB}{BE} = \frac{AC}{CE}$. Cross multiply: $(AB)(CE) = (BE)(AC)$. Next divide by $(CE)(AC)$ to get $\frac{(AB)(CE)}{(CE)(AC)} = \frac{(BE)(AC)}{(CE)(AC)}$, which reduces to $\frac{AB}{AC} = \frac{BE}{CE}$.

Solution to Proof #10.

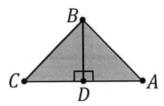

❶ $\overline{AB} \cong \overline{BC}$.	❶ Given.
❷ $\overline{AD} \cong \overline{CD}$.	❷ Def. of bisect.
❸ $\overline{BD}$ is common to $\triangle BAD$ and $\triangle BCD$.	❸ Reflexive prop.
❹ $\triangle BAD \cong \triangle BCD$.	❹ SSS (Steps 1-3).
❺ $\angle BAD \cong \angle BCD$. ∎	❺ CPCTC. ∎

Notes:

- The two small triangles are congruent because all three of their sides are congruent (SSS).
- CPCTC: Corresponding parts of congruent triangles are congruent.
- An isosceles triangle is a special case of the triangle bisector theorem (Proof 9). Segment $\overline{BD}$ is an angle bisector ($\angle CBD \cong \angle ABD$ according to the CPCTC) as well as a median (since it bisects $\overline{AC}$). According to the triangle bisector theorem, $\frac{CD}{AD} = \frac{BC}{AB}$; both fractions equal 1 for an isosceles triangle.

Solution to Proof #11.

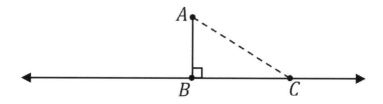

❶ $\overline{AB} \perp \overleftrightarrow{BC}$.	❶ Given.
❷ $\triangle ABC$ is a right triangle.	❷ Angle $\angle ABC$ is a right angle.
❸ $AC^2 = AB^2 + BC^2$.	❸ P.T.
❹ $BC^2 > 0$.	❹ BC is a distance. Distances are real. The square of any real number is positive.
❺ $AC^2 > AB^2$.	❺ Combine Steps 3-4.
❻ $AC > AB$. ∎	❻ Squareroot both sides of Step 5. ∎

Notes:

- Point C could be any point on the line except for point B.
- For any point C, we have shown that $AC > AB$.
- P.T. = Pythagorean theorem.

Solution to Proof #12.

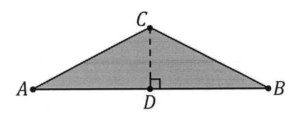

❶ $\overline{AD} \cong \overline{BD}$.	❶ Def. of bisect.
❷ $\overline{CD}$ is common to $\triangle ACD$ and $\triangle BCD$.	❷ Reflexive prop.
❸ $m\angle BDC = 90°$.	❸ Def. of perp.
❹ $\angle ADC \cong \angle BDC$.	❹ $\angle ADC$ and $\angle BDC$ are suppl.'s that form a straight line such that $m\angle ADC = 180° - 90° = 90°$.
❺ $\triangle ACD \cong \triangle BCD$.	❺ SAS (Steps 1, 2, and 4).
❻ $AC \cong BC$. ∎	❻ CPCTC. ∎

Notes:

- $m\angle ADC + m\angle BDC = 180°$ because $\angle ADC$ and $\angle BDC$ are supplements. Plug in $m\angle BDC = 90°$ to see that $m\angle ADC = 180° - 90° = 90°$.

- The two small triangles are congruent because two of their sides and the angle formed by those sides are congruent (SAS).

- CPCTC: Corresponding parts of congruent triangles are congruent.

Solution to Proof #13.

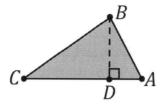

❶ ∠ADB is a right angle.	❶ Given.
❷ $\overline{BD} \perp \overline{AC}$.	❷ Def. of perpendicular.
❸ $\overline{AD}$ is the shortest possible straight connector from point A to line $\overleftrightarrow{BD}$.	❸ Follows from Step 2 and Proof 11.
❹ $\overline{CD}$ is the shortest possible straight connector from point C to line $\overleftrightarrow{BD}$.	❹ Follows from Step 2 and Proof 11.
❺ $AB > AD$.	❺ Follows from Step 3.
❻ $BC > CD$.	❻ Follows from Step 4.
❼ $AB + BC > AD + CD$.	❼ Add both sides of Eq.'s 5-6 together.
❽ $AD + CD = AC$.	❽ Prop. of addition.
❾ $AB + BC > AC$. ∎	❾ Sub. Step 8 into Step 7. ∎

Notes:

- In Proof 11, we showed that the shortest possible straight connector from a point to a line is perpendicular to the line.
- By drawing a perpendicular connector from A to $\overline{BC}$ or from C to $\overline{AB}$, we could similarly show that $AB + AC > BC$ and $AC + BC > AB$.

Solution to Proof #14.

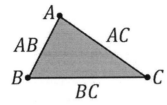

$$AB + BC > AC$$
$$BC + AC > AB$$
$$AC + AB > BC$$

❶ $AC + AB > BC$.	❶ The triangle inequality. Any side must be shorter than the sum of the other two sides.
❷ $AB > BC - AC$.	❷ Subtract AC from both sides of Step 1.
❸ $AB + BC > AC$.	❸ The triangle inequality. This time it is applied to side $\overline{AC}$.
❹ $AB > AC - BC$.	❹ Subtract BC from both sides of Step 3.
❺ $AB > |BC - AC|$. ∎	❺ Combine Steps 2 and 4 together. ∎

Notes:

- $AB > |BC - AC|$ means that $AB > BC - AC$ and $AB > -(BC - AC)$. The last inequality simplifies to $AB > -BC + AC$ when you distribute the minus sign, which is equivalent to $AB > AC - BC$. Thus, we see that $AB > |BC - AC|$ combines $AB > BC - AC$ and $AB > AC - BC$.

- It could similarly be shown that $BC > |AB - AC|$ and $AC > |AB - BC|$. In the next proof, we will see an example with numbers that helps to illustrate what these inequalities represent.

Solution to Proof #15.

$$6 + 8 = 14 \text{ cm}$$

6 cm   8 cm

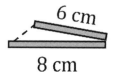

6 cm   8 cm

$$8 - 6$$
$$= 2 \text{ cm} \searrow$$ 6 cm

8 cm

6 cm

8 cm

❶ $BC = 6$ cm and $AC = 8$ cm.	❶ Given.
❷ $BC + AC > AB$.	❷ The triangle inequality. Any side must be shorter than the sum of the other two sides.
❸ $14 > AB$.	❸ Plug Step 1 into Step 2.
❹ $AB > \|BC - AC\|$.	❹ We showed this in Proof 14.
❺ $AB > 2$.	❺ Plug Step 1 into Step 4: $\|-2\| = 2$.
❻ $2 < AB < 14$. ∎	❻ Combine Steps 3 and 5 together. ∎

Notes:

- The top diagram shows that if the two given sides form an obtuse angle close to 180°, the third side is nearly equal to $6 + 8 = 14$ cm. The bottom diagram shows that if the two given sides form an acute angle close to 0°, the third side is nearly equal to $8 - 6 = 2$ cm.

- $14 > AB$ is equivalent to $AB < 14$ and $AB > 2$ is equivalent to $2 < AB$. Combine $2 < AB$ and $AB < 14$ to make $2 < AB < 14$.

Solution to Proof #16.

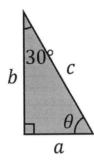 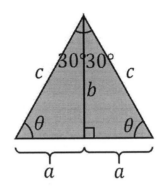

❶ The ang. meas. of one angle is 30°.

❷ The ang. meas. of one angle is 90°.

❸ $90° + 30° + \theta = 180°$.

❹ $\theta = 180° - 90° - 30° = 60°$.

❺ An equilateral triangle can be cut in half to form a 30° right triangle.

❻ $c = 2a$.

❼ $a^2 + b^2 = c^2$.

❽ $a^2 + b^2 = (2a)^2 = 4a^2$.

❾ $b^2 = 4a^2 - a^2 = 3a^2$
$b = a\sqrt{3}$.

❿ $\frac{b}{a} = \sqrt{3}$ and $\frac{c}{a} = 2$. ∎

---

❶ Given.

❷ Def. of right triangle.

❸ Angle sum thm.

❹ Solve for θ in Step 3.

❺ An equilateral triangle has angular measures of 60°. At the top, two 30° angles form a 60° angle. The bottom angles are $\theta = 60°$.

❻ An equilateral triangle has congr. sides. The bottom side ($2a$) is congr. with the top sides (c).

❼ P.T.

❽ Sub. Step 6 into Step 7.

❾ Solve for b in Step 8. Squareroot both sides of $b^2 = 3a^2$.

❿ Divide Steps 6 and 9 by a. ∎

Solution to Proof #17.

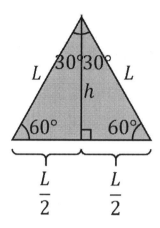

❶ Each edge has length L.

❷ The angular measures are 60°.

❸ An equilateral triangle can be cut in half to form a 30° right triangle.

❹ The base of the 30°-60°-90° triangle is $\frac{L}{2}$.

❺ The height of the 30°-60°-90° triangle is $\frac{L\sqrt{3}}{2}$.

❻ The area of the 30°-60°-90° triangle is $\frac{1}{2}\left(\frac{L}{2}\right)\left(\frac{L\sqrt{3}}{2}\right) = \frac{L^2\sqrt{3}}{8}$.

❼ The area of the equilateral triangle is $2\left(\frac{L^2\sqrt{3}}{8}\right) = \frac{L^2\sqrt{3}}{4}$. ∎

❶ Def. of equilateral.

❷ Equilateral triangles are equiangular.

❸ As shown above. See the solution to Proof 16.

❹ In Proof 16, we showed that the side opposite to the 30° is half as long as the hypotenuse.

❺ In Proof 16, we showed that the side opposite to the 60° is $\sqrt{3}$ times as long as the side opposite to the 30° angle. Mult. Step 4 by $\sqrt{3}$.

❻ The area of a triangle is one-half its base $\left(\frac{L}{2}\right)$ times its height $\left(\frac{L\sqrt{3}}{2}\right)$.

❼ Mult. Step 6 by 2. The equilateral triangle has twice the area of the 30°-60°-90° triangle. ∎

Solution to Proof #18.

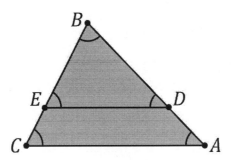

❶ $\overline{AC} \parallel \overline{DE}$.	❶ Given.
❷ $\overline{AB}$ and $\overline{BC}$ are transversals.	❷ Def. of transversal.
❸ $\angle BED \cong \angle BCA$ and $\angle BDE \cong \angle BAC$.	❸ Corresponding angles.
❹ $\triangle ABC \sim \triangle DBE$. ∎	❹ Two angles are congr. (Step 3). ∎

Notes:

- When two parallel lines are cut by a transversal, corresponding angles are congruent. We proved this in Example 3.
- When two pairs of corresponding angles are congruent, triangles are similar. (The third pair of angles is also congruent according to the angle sum theorem, though in this problem it shouldn't be necessary to use the angle sum theorem to see this.)

Solution to Proof #19.

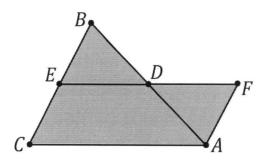

❶ $\overline{BD} \cong \overline{AD}$.

❷ $\overline{DE} \cong \overline{DF}$ (and thus $DE = DF$).

❸ $\angle BDE \cong \angle ADF$.

❹ $\triangle BDE \cong \triangle ADF$.

❺ $\overline{BE} \cong \overline{AF}$.

❻ $\overline{BE} \cong \overline{CE}$.

❼ $\overline{CE} \cong \overline{AF}$.

❽ $DE + DF = EF$.

❾ $DE + DE = 2DE = EF$ and $DE = \frac{EF}{2}$.

❿ $\angle EBD \cong \angle FAD$.

⓫ $\overline{BC} \parallel \overline{AF}$.

⓬ $ACEF$ is a parallelogram.

⓭ $\overline{AC} \cong \overline{EF}$, $\overline{AC} \parallel \overline{EF}$, and $DE = \frac{AC}{2}$. ∎

❶ Def. of bisect.

❷ Given.

❸ Vertical angles.

❹ SAS (Steps 1-3).

❺ CPCTC.

❻ Def. of bisect.

❼ Transitive prop. (Steps 5-6).

❽ Prop. of addition.

❾ Sub. Step 2 into Step 8.

❿ CPCTC.

⓫ Step 10 involves alt. int. angles.

⓬ Follows from Steps 7 and 11.

⓭ The first two parts follow from Step 12. The last part uses Step 9. ∎

Solution to Proof #20.

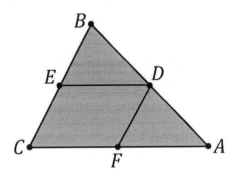

❶ Points D, E, and F bisect their respective sides.	❶ Def. of midpoint.
❷ $\overline{DE} \parallel \overline{AC}$.	❷ This follows from Step 1 according to the results of Proof 19.
❸ $\triangle BDE \sim \triangle BAC$.	❸ This follows from Step 2 according to the result of Proof 18.
❹ $\angle DBE \cong \angle ADF$ and $\angle BDE \cong \angle DAF$.	❹ Similar triangles are equiangular.
❺ $\overline{BD} \cong \overline{AD}$.	❺ Def. of midpoint.
❻ $\triangle BDE \cong \triangle DAF$. ∎	❻ ASA (Steps 4-5). ∎

Solution to Proof #21.

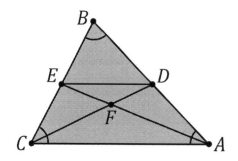

❶ Points D and E bisect their respective sides.	❶ Def. of midpoint.
❷ $\overline{DE} \parallel \overline{AC}$.	❷ This follows from Step 1 according to the results of Proof 19.
❸ $\angle DEF \cong \angle CAF$ and $\angle EDF \cong \angle ACF$.	❸ Alt. int. angles.
❹ $\triangle DEF \sim \triangle CAF$.	❹ Two angles are congruent (Step 3).
❺ $DE = \frac{AC}{2}$.	❺ This follows from Step 1 according to the results of Proof 19.
❻ $EF = \frac{AF}{2}$ and $DF = \frac{CF}{2}$. ■	❻ The sides of similar triangles come in the same proportions. ■

Notes:

- $\overline{AE}$ and $\overline{CD}$ are medians. $\overline{BF}$ is also part of a median. All three medians intersect at a single point (labeled F) called the centroid. The medians are said to be concurrent.

- The centroid (point F) is one-third of the distance from the midpoint to its opposite vertex. For example, DF is one-third of CD (since $DF = \frac{CF}{2}$, which can be rewritten $2DF = CF$, and since $DF + CF = DF + 2DF = 3DF = CD$, which can be rewritten $DF = \frac{CD}{3}$).

Solution to Proof #22.

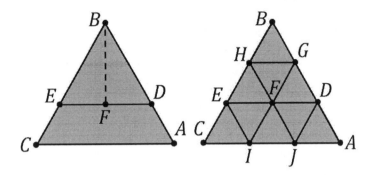

❶ Point F is the centroid, where the three medians intersect.	❶ Given.
❷ $\overline{DE}$, $\overline{GI}$, and $\overline{HJ}$ are parallel to one side of triangle $\triangle ABC$.	❷ This follows from Step 1 according to the results of Proofs 19-21.
❸ $\triangle ABC$ is equilateral.	❸ Given.
❹ $m\angle ABC = m\angle BCA = m\angle CAB = 60°$.	❹ Prop. of equilateral triangle.
❺ The interior angles of all of the upright triangles are 60°.	❺ Corresponding angles with $\triangle ABC$.
❻ The interior angles of all of the inverted triangles are 60°.	❻ Angles forming a straight line add to 180°. Ex.: $\angle CEI + \angle FEI + \angle FEH$.
❼ Point F is one-third of the distance between each midpoint of $\triangle ABC$ and its opposite vertex.	❼ We showed this in Proof 21. See the notes to Solution 21.
❽ Each small triangle has an edge length that is one-third the edge length of $\triangle ABC$.	❽ The edges of 3 small triangles join together at the edges of $\triangle ABC$. The height of the triangles are also one-third of the height of $\triangle ABC$, agreeing with Step 7.
❾ The 9 small triangles are congruent and fit perfectly into $\triangle ABC$. ∎	❾ SSS and Step 8. ∎

Solution to Proof #23.

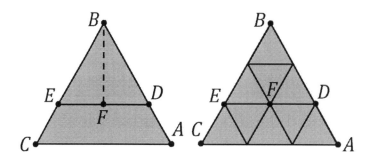

❶ The 9 small triangles are congruent and fit perfectly into $\triangle ABC$.	❶ We showed this in Proof 22.
❷ The 9 small triangles have the same area. Call this area A.	❷ Follows from Step 1.
❸ The area of triangle $\triangle DBE$ is $4A$.	❸ $\triangle DBE$ divides into 4 small triangles.
❹ The area of trapezoid $ACED$ is $5A$.	❹ $ACED$ divides into 5 small triangles.
❺ The ratio of the area of trapezoid $ACED$ to the area of triangle $\triangle DBE$ is 5:4. ∎	❺ Divide Step 4 by Step 3: $\frac{5A}{4A} = \frac{5}{4}$. ∎

Note:

- The centroid is known as the center of mass because it serves as the balancing point. At the center of mass, the torques are balanced, not the weights. If you have any experience sitting on a seesaw at a playground, you should know that the heavier child should sit closer to the fulcrum in order to balance the seesaw. Similarly, in the picture above, trapezoid $ACED$ is closer on average to the centroid (point F) while triangle $\triangle DBE$ is further on average from the centroid. This is why the trapezoid has more area (and thus more mass) than the triangle.

Solution to Proof #24.

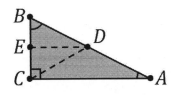

❶ The midsegment, $\overline{DE}$, is the line segment that bisects $\overline{AB}$ and $\overline{BC}$. Points D and E are midpoints of their respective sides.

❷ $\overline{DE} \parallel \overline{AC}$.

❸ $m\angle ACE = 90°$.

❹ $m\angle ACE + m\angle CED = 180°$.

❺ $90° + m\angle CED = 180°$.

❻ $m\angle CED = 180° - 90° = 90°$.

❼ $\angle ACE \cong \angle CED$.

❽ $\angle BED \cong \angle CED$.

❾ $\overline{BE} \cong \overline{EC}$.

❿ $\overline{DE}$ is common to $\triangle BDE$ and $\triangle CDE$.

⓫ $\triangle BDE \cong \triangle CDE$.

⓬ $\overline{BD} \cong \overline{CD} \cong \overline{AD}$. ∎

❶ Def. of midsegment. See Proof 19. It was given that point D is a midpoint.

❷ Follows from Step 1. We showed this in Proof 19.

❸ Def. of right triangle.

❹ The parallel postulate. (If this were not true, lines $\overleftrightarrow{DE}$ and $\overleftrightarrow{AC}$ would eventually intersect.)

❺ Sub. Step 3 into Step 4.

❻ Subtract 90° from both sides of Step 5.

❼ Compare Steps 3 and 6.

❽ Suppl. angles and $m\angle CED = 90°$ (Step 6).

❾ Point E is a midpoint (Step 1).

❿ Reflexive property.

⓫ SAS (Steps 8-10).

⓬ CPCTC and point D is a midpoint. ∎

Solution to Proof #25.

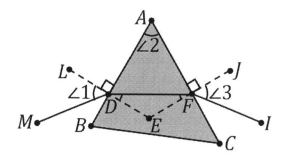

❶ $\angle EDF \cong \angle EFD$.	❶ Given.
❷ $m\angle EDF + m\angle EFD + m\angle DEF = 180°$.	❷ Angle sum thm. for triangle ΔDEF.
❸ $2(m\angle EDF) + m\angle DEF = 180°$.	❸ Sub. Step 1 into Step 2.
❹ $\overline{LE} \perp \overline{AB}$ and $\overline{EJ} \perp \overline{AC}$.	❹ Given.
❺ $m\angle ADE = m\angle AFE = 90°$.	❺ Def. of perpendicular.
❻ $m\angle 2 + m\angle ADE + m\angle DEF + m\angle AFE = 360°$.	❻ Angle sum thm. for quad. $ADEF$.
❼ $m\angle 2 + 90° + m\angle DEF + 90° = 360°$.	❼ Sub. Step 5 into Step 6.
❽ $m\angle 2 + m\angle DEF = 180°$.	❽ Subtract 180° from both sides of Step 7.
❾ $2(m\angle EDF) + m\angle DEF = m\angle 2 + m\angle DEF$.	❾ Set Eq.'s 3 and 8 equal to each other.
❿ $2\,m\angle EDF = m\angle 2$. ∎	❿ Subtract $m\angle DEF$ from both sides of Step 9. ∎

Note:

- Proofs 25-26 have an application in prism spectroscopy.

Solution to Proof #26.

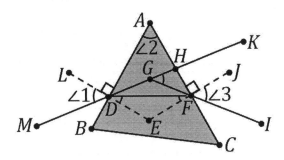

❶ $\angle 1 \cong \angle 3$.	**❶** Given.
❷ $\angle GDE \cong \angle 1 \cong \angle 3 \cong \angle GFE$.	**❷** Vertical angles and Step 1.
❸ $m\angle GDF = m\angle 1 - m\angle EDF$ $= m\angle GFD = m\angle 1 - m\angle EFD$.	**❸** Prop. of subtraction and Step 2.
❹ $m\angle GDF + m\angle DGF + m\angle GFD$ $= 180°$.	**❹** Angle sum thm. for triangle $\triangle DGF$.
❺ $2(m\angle GDF) + m\angle DGF = 180°$.	**❺** Sub. Step 3 ($m\angle GDF = m\angle GFD$) into Step 4.
❻ $m\angle DGF + m\angle KGI = 180°$.	**❻** Suppl. angles.
❼ $2(m\angle GDF) + m\angle DGF$ $= m\angle DGF + m\angle KGI$.	**❼** Set Eq.'s 5-6 equal to each other.
❽ $2(m\angle GDF) = m\angle KGI$.	**❽** Subtract $m\angle DGF$ from both sides of Step 7.
❾ $2(m\angle 1 - m\angle EDF) = m\angle KGI$. ∎	**❾** Sub. Step 3 ($m\angle GDF = m\angle 1$ $-m\angle EDF$) into Step 8. ∎

Solution to Proof #27.

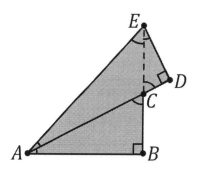

❶ $m\angle ABC = 90°$ and $m\angle ADE = 90°$.	❶ Given.
❷ $\angle ABC \cong \angle CDE$.	❷ Both are right angles (Step 1).
❸ $\angle ACB \cong \angle DCE$.	❸ Vertical angles.
❹ $\triangle ABC \sim \triangle CDE$. ∎	❹ Two angles are congr. (Steps 2-3). ∎

Note:

- When two pairs of corresponding angles are congruent, triangles are similar. (The third pair of angles is also congruent according to the angle sum theorem.)

Solution to Proof #28.

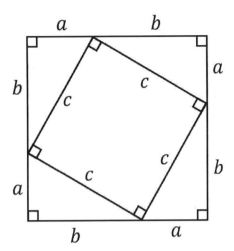

❶ The length of the large square is $a + b$.	❶ Given.
❷ The area of the large square is $(a + b)^2$.	❷ Formula for the area of a square.
❸ The area of the large square is $a^2 + 2ab + b^2$.	❸ Apply the f.o.i.l. method of algebra to Step 2.
❹ The area of the small square is c^2.	❹ Formula for the area of a square.
❺ The area of each right triangle is $\frac{1}{2}ab$.	❺ Formula for the area of a triangle with base b and height a.
❻ The area of the large square is $c^2 + 4\left(\frac{1}{2}ab\right)$.	❻ Add the areas of the small square and four right triangles together.
❼ The area of the large square is $c^2 + 2ab$.	❼ Simplify Step 6: $4\left(\frac{1}{2}ab\right) = 2ab$.
❽ $a^2 + 2ab + b^2 = c^2 + 2ab$.	❽ Set Steps 3 and 7 equal to each other.
❾ $a^2 + b^2 = c^2$. ■	❾ Subtract $2ab$ from both sides of Step 8. ■

Solution to Proof #29.

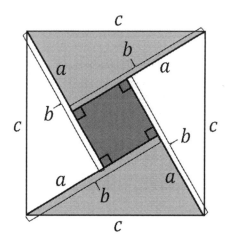

❶ The area of the large square is c^2.

❷ The length of the small square is $b - a$.

❸ The area of the small square is $(b - a)^2$.

❹ The area of the small square is $b^2 - 2ab + a^2$.

❺ The area of each right triangle is $\frac{1}{2}ab$.

❻ The area of the large square is $b^2 - 2ab + a^2 + 4\left(\frac{1}{2}ab\right)$.

❼ The area of the large square is $b^2 - 2ab + a^2 + 2ab$.

❽ The area of the large square is $b^2 + a^2$.

❾ $b^2 + a^2 = c^2$. ∎

❶ Formula for the area of a square.

❷ Given.

❸ Formula for the area of a square.

❹ Apply the f.o.i.l. method of algebra to Step 3.

❺ Formula for the area of a triangle with base a and height b.

❻ Add the areas of the small square and four right triangles together.

❼ Simplify Step 6: $4\left(\frac{1}{2}ab\right) = 2ab$.

❽ Simplify Step 7: $2ab$ cancels out.

❾ Set Steps 1 and 8 equal to each other. ∎

Solution to Proof #30.

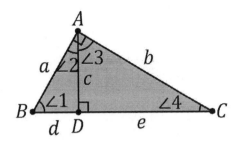

❶ $\angle ADB \cong \angle ADC \cong \angle BAC$.	**❶** All are right angles.
❷ $m\angle ADB = m\angle ADC = m\angle BAC = 90°$.	**❷** Def. of right angle.
❸ $m\angle 2 + m\angle 3 = 90°$.	**❸** Compl. angles.
❹ $m\angle 1 + m\angle 2 + 90° = 180°$. $m\angle 3 + m\angle 4 + 90° = 180°$. $m\angle 1 + m\angle 4 + 90° = 180°$.	**❹** Angle sum thm.
❺ $m\angle 1 + m\angle 2 = 90°$. $m\angle 3 + m\angle 4 = 90°$. $m\angle 1 + m\angle 4 = 90°$.	**❺** Subtract 90° from both sides of each eq. in Step 4.
❻ $\angle 1 \cong \angle 3$ and $\angle 2 \cong \angle 4$.	**❻** Compare Steps 3 and 5.
❼ $\triangle ADB \sim \triangle ADC \sim \triangle BAC$.	**❼** Two angles are congr. (Steps 1 and 6).
❽ $a:c:d = b:e:c = (d+e):b:a$.	**❽** Corresponding sides of similar triangles come in the same proportions.
❾ $\frac{c}{d} = \frac{e}{c}$ and $\frac{b}{e} = \frac{d+e}{b}$.	**❾** $c:d = e:c$ and $b:e = (d+e):b$ in Step 8.
❿ $c^2 = ed$ and $b^2 = de + e^2$.	**❿** Cross multiply in Step 9.
⓫ $b^2 = c^2 + e^2$. ∎	**⓫** Sub. $c^2 = ed$ into $b^2 = de + e^2$. ∎

Solution to Proof #31.

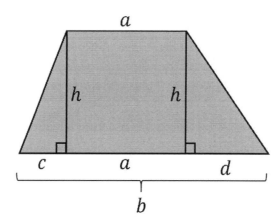

❶ The area of the rectangle is ah.

❷ The area of the triangle on the left is $\frac{1}{2}ch$.

❸ The area of the triangle on the right is $\frac{1}{2}dh$.

❹ The area of the trapezoid is $ah + \frac{1}{2}ch + \frac{1}{2}dh$.

❺ The area of the trapezoid is $\frac{1}{2}(2a + c + d)h$.

❻ $2a + c + d = a + (a + c + d)$ $= a + b$.

❼ The area of the trapezoid is $\frac{1}{2}(a + b)h$. ∎

❶ Formula for the area of a rectangle with width a and height h.

❷ Formula for the area of a triangle with base c and height h.

❸ Formula for the area of a triangle with base d and height h.

❹ Add the formulas from Steps 1-3. The area of a region equals the sum of the areas of its non-overlapping parts.

❺ Factor out $\frac{1}{2}h$ from Step 4. Note that $\frac{1}{2}(2a + c + d) = a + \frac{c}{2} + \frac{d}{2}$.

❻ Algebra: $2a = a + a$. Note that $a + c + d = b$.

❼ Sub. Step 6 into Step 5. ∎

Solution to Proof #32.

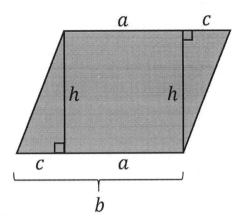

❶ The area of the rectangle is ah.

❷ The area of the triangle on the left is $\frac{1}{2}ch$.

❸ The area of the triangle on the right is $\frac{1}{2}ch$.

❹ The area of the parallelogram is $ah + \frac{1}{2}ch + \frac{1}{2}ch$.

❺ The area of the parallelogram is $ah + ch = (a + c)h$.

❻ $a + c = b$.

❼ The area of the parallelogram is bh. ∎

❶ Formula for the area of a rectangle with width a and height h.

❷ Formula for the area of a triangle with base c and height h.

❸ Formula for the area of a triangle with base c and height h.

❹ Add the formulas from Steps 1-3. The area of a region equals the sum of the areas of its non-overlapping parts.

❺ Simplify Step 4. Note that $\frac{1}{2} + \frac{1}{2} = 1$. Factor out the h.

❻ Prop. of addition.

❼ Sub. Step 6 into Step 5. ∎

Solution to Proof #33.

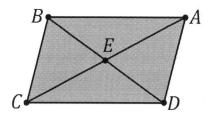

❶ $\overline{AB} \parallel \overline{CD}$ and $\overline{BC} \parallel \overline{AD}$.	❶ Def. of parallelogram.
❷ $\overline{AB} \cong \overline{CD}$.	❷ Prop. of parallelogram. See Example 6.
❸ $\angle ABD \cong \angle CDB$ and $\angle BAC \cong \angle DCA$.	❸ Alt. int. angles.
❹ $\triangle BAE \cong \triangle CDE$.	❹ ASA (Steps 2-3).
❺ $\overline{BE} \cong \overline{DE}$ and $\overline{CE} \cong \overline{AE}$. ∎	❺ CPCTC. ∎

Notes:

- In Example 6, we proved that the diagonal divides the parallelogram into two congruent triangles, from which it follows (according to the CPCTC) that opposite edges of a parallelogram are congruent.
- In Proof 33, we are proving that the two diagonals divide the parallelogram into two pairs of congruent triangles (there are 4 triangles here, compared to 2 triangles in Example 6).

Solution to Proof #34.

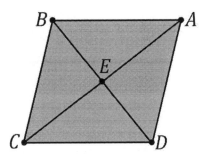

❶ $\overline{AB} \cong \overline{BC} \cong \overline{CD} \cong \overline{AD}$.	❶ Def. of rhombus.
❷ $\overline{BE} \cong \overline{DE}$ and $\overline{CE} \cong \overline{AE}$.	❷ Prop. of parallelogram. We showed this in Proof 33.
❸ $\overline{AE}$ is common to ΔBAE and ΔDAE.	❸ Reflexive prop.
❹ $\Delta BAE \cong \Delta DAE$.	❹ SSS (Steps 1-3).
❺ $\angle AEB \cong \angle AED$.	❺ CPCTC.
❻ $m\angle AEB + m\angle AED = 180°$.	❻ Suppl. angles.
❼ $m\angle AEB + m\angle AEB = 180°$.	❼ Sub. Step 5 into Step 6.
❽ $2m\angle AEB = 180°$.	❽ Simplify Step 7.
❾ $m\angle AEB = m\angle AED = 90°$. ∎	❾ Divide both sides of Step 8 by 2. Also use Step 5. ∎

Note:

- The diagonals of a rhombus or a square are perpendicular to each other. This is not true for other types of parallelograms. (However, we will see in Proof 36 that this is true for a kite, which isn't a parallelogram.)

Solution to Proof #35.

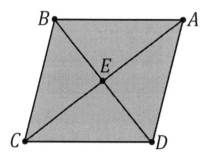

❶ $\overline{AB} \cong \overline{BC} \cong \overline{CD} \cong \overline{AD}$.	❶ Def. of rhombus.
❷ $\overline{BE} \cong \overline{DE}$ and $\overline{CE} \cong \overline{AE}$.	❷ Prop. of parallelogram. We showed this in Proof 33.
❸ $\overline{AE}$ is common to ΔBAE and ΔDAE.	❸ Reflexive prop.
❹ $\Delta BAE \cong \Delta DAE$.	❹ SSS (Steps 1-3).
❺ $\angle BAE \cong \angle DAE$. ∎	❺ CPCTC. ∎

Notes:

- It can similarly be shown that $\Delta CBE \cong \Delta ABE$ and $\angle CBE \cong \angle ABE$.
- The diagonals of a rhombus or a square bisect the interior angles. This is not true for other types of parallelograms.

Solution to Proof #36.

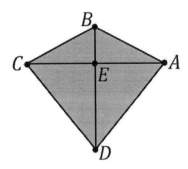

❶ $\overline{AB} \cong \overline{BC}$ and $\overline{CD} \cong \overline{AD}$.	❶ Given.
❷ $\overline{BD}$ is common to $\triangle BCD$ and $\triangle BAD$.	❷ Reflexive prop.
❸ $\triangle BCD \cong \triangle BAD$.	❸ SSS (Steps 1-3).
❹ $\angle CBD \cong \angle ABD$.	❹ CPCTC.
❺ $\overline{BE}$ is common to $\triangle BCE$ and $\triangle BAE$.	❺ Reflexive prop.
❻ $\triangle BCE \cong \triangle BAE$.	❻ SAS (Steps 1, 4, and 5).
❼ $\angle BEC \cong \angle BEA$.	❼ CPCTC.
❽ $m\angle BEC + m\angle BEA = 180°$.	❽ Suppl. angles.
❾ $m\angle BEC + m\angle BEC = 180°$.	❾ Sub. Step 7 into Step 8.
❿ $2m\angle BEC = 180°$.	❿ Simplify Step 9.
⓫ $m\angle BEC = m\angle BEA = 90°.$ ∎	⓫ Divide both sides of Step 10 by 2. Also use Step 7. ∎

Solution to Proof #37.

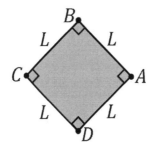
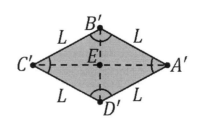

❶ The rhombus can be divided into 4 congruent right triangles as shown above on the right.

❶ See the solution (and notes) to Proofs 34-35.

❷ $m\angle B'A'D' = 60°$.

❷ Given.

❸ $\angle D'C'B' \cong \angle B'A'D'$ and $\angle C'B'A' \cong \angle A'D'C'$.

❸ See Example 5 and its notes.

❹ $m\angle B'A'D' + m\angle A'D'C' + m\angle D'C'B' + m\angle C'B'A' = 360°$.

❹ The sum of the angular measures of the interior angles of a quad. add up to 360°.

❺ $2(m\angle B'A'D') + 2(m\angle C'B'A') = 360°$.

❺ Sub. Step 3 into Step 4.

❻ $2(60°) + 2(m\angle C'B'A') = 360°$.

❻ Sub. Step 2 into Step 5.

❼ $m\angle C'B'A' = 120°$.

❼ Solve for $m\angle C'B'A'$ in Step 6.

❽ $m\angle B'A'E' = 30°, m\angle A'B'E' = 60°$.

❽ Bisect the angles of Steps 2 and 7.

❾ Each right triangle has area $\frac{L^2\sqrt{3}}{8}$.

❾ One-half the area of Proof 17.

❿ The area of the rhombus is $\frac{L^2\sqrt{3}}{2}$.

❿ Multiply Step 9 by 4.

⓫ The area of the square is L^2.

⓫ Formula for the area of a square.

⓬ $\frac{A_{rhombus}}{A_{square}} = \frac{L^2\sqrt{3}}{2L^2} = \frac{\sqrt{3}}{2}$. ■

⓬ Divide Step 10 by Step 11. ■

Solution to Proof #38.

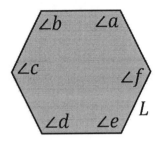
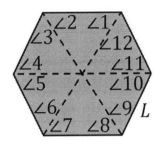

❶ $\angle a \cong \angle b \cong \angle c \cong \cdots \cong \angle f$ and the length of each edge is L.

❷ $m\angle a = 180° - \frac{360°}{6} = 120°$.

❸ The hexagon can be divided into 6 congruent triangles as shown above on the right.

❹ $m\angle 1 = m\angle 2 = \cdots = m\angle 12 = 60°$.

❺ The 6 triangles are equiangular.

❻ The 6 triangles are equilateral.

❼ The area of each equilateral triangle is $\frac{L^2\sqrt{3}}{4}$.

❽ The area of the hexagon is $\frac{6L^2\sqrt{3}}{4}$.

❾ The area of the hexagon is $\frac{3L^2\sqrt{3}}{2}$. ∎

❶ A regular hexagon is equiangular and equilateral.

❷ Set $N = 6$ in the result of Proof 7.

❸ Connect the center of the hexagon to each vertex.

❹ By symmetry, divide Step 2 by 2.

❺ Angle sum thm. The ang. meas. of the third angle is also 60°.

❻ An equiangular triangle is also equilateral.

❼ We showed this in Proof 17.

❽ Multiply Step 7 by 6.

❾ Reduce $\frac{6}{4}$ down to $\frac{3}{2}$. ∎

Solution to Proof #39.

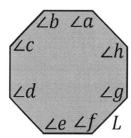
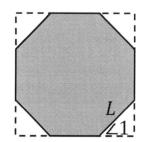

❶ The int. and ext. angles are congr. and the length of each edge is L.

❷ $m\angle 1 = \frac{360°}{8} = 45°$ is the angular measure of each exterior angle.

❸ Each triangle is a 45°-45°-90° triangle.

❹ The hypotenuse of each triangle is L.

❺ The legs of each triangle are $\frac{L}{\sqrt{2}}$.

❻ The area of each triangle is $\frac{1}{2}\left(\frac{L}{\sqrt{2}}\right)\left(\frac{L}{\sqrt{2}}\right) = \frac{L^2}{4}$.

❼ The square has edge length $L + \frac{L}{\sqrt{2}} + \frac{L}{\sqrt{2}} = L + \frac{2L}{\sqrt{2}} = L + L\sqrt{2}$.

❽ The area of the square is $\left(L + L\sqrt{2}\right)^2$ $= L^2 + 2L^2\sqrt{2} + 2L^2 = 3L^2 + 2L^2\sqrt{2}$.

❾ The area of the octagon is
$$3L^2 + 2L^2\sqrt{2} - 4\left(\frac{L^2}{4}\right) = 2L^2 + 2L^2\sqrt{2}$$
$$= 2L^2\left(1 + \sqrt{2}\right). \blacksquare$$

❶ A regular octagon is equiangular and equilateral.

❷ Set $N = 8$ in the result of Proof 8.

❸ Two of the interior angles of each triangle are exterior angles of the hexagon. From the angle sum thm., the third ang. meas. is 90°.

❹ Given.

❺ The edges of a 45° right triangle come in the ratio $1:1:\sqrt{2}$. (See Example 4.) Divide the hypotenuse by $\sqrt{2}$.

❻ The area of a triangle equals one-half its base times its height.

❼ Prop. of addition. Note that $\frac{2}{\sqrt{2}} = \sqrt{2}$ since $\sqrt{2}\sqrt{2} = 2$.

❽ Formula for the area of a square. Use the f.o.i.l. method of algebra.

❾ Subtract the area of 4 triangles from the area of the square. Factor out $2L^2$. $\blacksquare$

Solution to Proof #40.

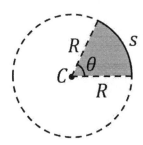

❶ There are 2π radians in a full circle.	❶ $360° = 2\pi$ radians.
❷ $C = 2\pi R$ is the circumf.	❷ Formula for circumf.
❸ s is a fraction of C. $m\angle\theta$ is a fraction of 2π. These fractions are equal.	❸ Prop. of division. Example: Halfway around a circle is π rad and half the circumf.
❹ $\frac{s}{C} = \frac{m\angle\theta}{2\pi}$.	❹ The proportionality from Step 3.
❺ $s = \frac{(m\angle\theta)C}{2\pi}$.	❺ Multiply both sides of Step 4 by C.
❻ $s = \frac{(m\angle\theta)2\pi R}{2\pi}$.	❻ Sub. Step 2 into Step 5.
❼ $s = R\,(m\angle\theta)$. ∎	❼ Simplify Step 6: Note that $\frac{2\pi}{2\pi} = 1$. ∎

Notes:

- $\angle\theta$ is a central angle: $m\angle\theta$ is measured from the center (point C).
- $m\angle\theta$ must be expressed in radians (since we used 2π radians for the angular measure of the central angle for one full circle in our proof).

Solution to Proof #41.

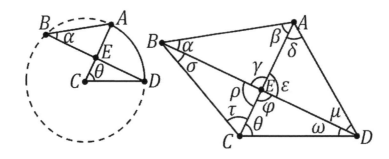

❶ The center of the circle is at point C.	❶ Given.
❷ $BC = AC = CD = R$.	❷ A radius extends from point C to the edge of the circle.
❸ $\triangle ABC$ is an isosceles triangle.	❸ $BC = AC = R$ (Step 2).
❹ $\triangle ADC$ is an isosceles triangle.	❹ $AC = CD = R$ (Step 2).
❺ $\triangle BCD$ is an isosceles triangle.	❺ $BC = CD = R$ (Step 2).
❻ $m\angle\beta = m\angle\alpha + m\angle\sigma$.	❻ The angles opposite to the congr. sides of an isosceles triangle are congr. (We demonstrated this in Proof 10.) In $\triangle ABC$, $BC = AC$.
❼ $m\angle\delta = m\angle\omega + m\angle\mu$.	❼ The angles opposite to the congr. sides of an isosceles triangle are congr. In $\triangle ADC$, $AC = CD$.
❽ $\angle\omega \cong \angle\sigma$. ∎	❽ The angles opposite to the congr. sides of an isosceles triangle are congr. In $\triangle BCD$, $BC = CD$. ∎

Solution to Proof #42.

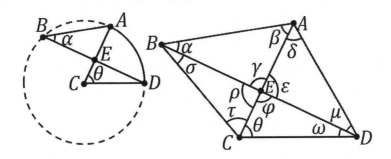

❶ $m\angle\beta = m\angle\alpha + m\angle\sigma$,
$m\angle\delta = m\angle\omega + m\angle\mu$,
and $\angle\omega \cong \angle\sigma$.

❷ $m\angle\delta = m\angle\sigma + m\angle\mu$.

❸ $m\angle\alpha + m\angle\beta + m\angle\delta + m\angle\mu$
$= 180°$.

❹ $m\angle\alpha + (m\angle\alpha + m\angle\sigma)$
$+ m\angle\delta + m\angle\mu = 180°$.

❺ $2(m\angle\alpha) + m\angle\sigma + m\angle\delta + m\angle\mu$
$= 180°$.

❻ $2(m\angle\alpha) + 2(m\angle\delta) = 180°$.

❼ $m\angle\alpha + m\angle\delta = 90°$. ∎

❶ We showed this in Proof 41.

❷ In Step 1, sub. $\angle\omega \cong \angle\sigma$ into
$m\angle\delta = m\angle\omega + m\angle\mu$.

❸ Angle sum thm. for triangle $\triangle BAD$.

❹ Sub. $\angle\beta = m\angle\alpha + m\angle\sigma$ from Step 1
into Step 3.

❺ Simplify Step 4.

❻ Sub. $m\angle\delta = m\angle\sigma + m\angle\mu$ from Step
2 into Step 5.

❼ Divide both sides of Step 6 by 2. ∎

Solution to Proof #43.

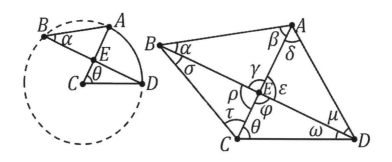

❶ $m\angle\alpha + m\angle\delta = 90°$.

❷ $m\angle\theta + m\angle\omega + m\angle\mu + m\angle\delta$
$\quad = 180°$.

❸ $m\angle\delta = m\angle\omega + m\angle\mu$.

❹ $m\angle\theta + m\angle\delta + m\angle\delta = 180°$.

❺ $m\angle\theta + 2(m\angle\delta) = 180°$.

❻ $\frac{m\angle\theta}{2} + m\angle\delta = 90°$.

❼ $m\angle\alpha + m\angle\delta = \frac{m\angle\theta}{2} + m\angle\delta$.

❽ $m\angle\alpha = \frac{m\angle\theta}{2}$. ∎

❶ We showed this in Proof 42.

❷ Angle sum thm. for triangle $\triangle ACD$.

❸ We showed this in Proof 41.

❹ Sub. Step 3 into Step 2.

❺ Simplify Step 4.

❻ Divide both sides of Step 5 by 2.

❼ Set Eq.'s 1 and 6 equal to each other.

❽ Subtract $m\angle\delta$ from both sides of Step 7. ∎

Solution to Proof #44.

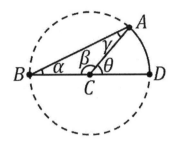

❶ The center of the circle is at point C.	❶ Given.
❷ $BC = AC = CD = R$.	❷ A radius extends from point C to the edge of the circle.
❸ $\triangle ABC$ is an isosceles triangle.	❸ $BC = AC = R$ (Step 2).
❹ $\angle\alpha \cong \angle\gamma$.	❹ The angles opposite to the congr. sides of an isosceles triangle are congr. (We demonstrated this in Proof 10.) In $\triangle ABC$, $BC = AC$.
❺ $m\angle\alpha + m\angle\gamma + m\angle\beta = 180°$.	❺ Angle sum thm. for triangle $\triangle ABC$.
❻ $m\angle\alpha + m\angle\alpha + m\angle\beta = 180°$.	❻ Sub. Step 4 into Step 5.
❼ $2(m\angle\alpha) + m\angle\beta = 180°$.	❼ Simplify Step 6.
❽ $m\angle\beta + m\angle\theta = 180°$.	❽ Suppl. angles.
❾ $2(m\angle\alpha) + m\angle\beta = m\angle\beta + m\angle\theta$.	❾ Set Eq.'s 7 and 8 equal to each other.
❿ $2(m\angle\alpha) = m\angle\theta$.	❿ Subtract $m\angle\beta$ from both sides of Step 9.
⓫ $m\angle\alpha = \dfrac{m\angle\theta}{2}$. ■	⓫ Divide both sides of Step 10 by 2. ■

Solution to Proof #45.

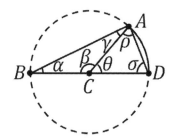

❶ The center of the circle is at point C.

❷ $BC = AC = CD = R$.

❸ $\triangle ABC$ and $\triangle ADC$ are isosceles triangles.

❹ $\angle\alpha \cong \angle\gamma$ and $\angle\rho \cong \angle\sigma$.

❺ $m\angle\alpha + m\angle\gamma + m\angle\beta = 180°$.
$m\angle\theta + m\angle\rho + m\angle\sigma = 180°$.

❻ $2(m\angle\gamma) + m\angle\beta = 180°$.
$m\angle\theta + 2(m\angle\rho) = 180°$.

❼ $2(m\angle\gamma) + m\angle\beta + m\angle\theta + 2(m\angle\rho)$
$= 360°$.

❽ $m\angle\beta + m\angle\theta = 180°$.

❾ $2(m\angle\gamma) + 180° + 2(m\angle\rho) = 360°$.

❿ $2(m\angle\gamma) + 2(m\angle\rho) = 180°$.

⓫ $m\angle\gamma + m\angle\rho = 90°$. ∎

❶ Given.

❷ A radius extends from point C to the edge of the circle.

❸ Two sides of each triangle are congr. (Step 2).

❹ The angles opposite to the congr. sides of an isosceles triangle are congr. (We demonstrated this in Proof 10.)

❺ Angle sum thm. for triangles $\triangle ABC$ and $\triangle ADC$.

❻ Sub. Step 4 into Step 5 and simplify.

❼ Add both sides of Eq. 6 together.

❽ Suppl. angles.

❾ Sub. Step 8 into Step 7.

❿ Subtract 180° from both sides of Step 9.

⓫ Divide both sides of Step 10 by 2. ∎

Solution to Proof #46.

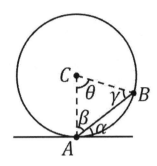

❶ The center of the circle is at point C.	❶ Given.
❷ $AC = BC = R$.	❷ A radius extends from point C to the edge of the circle.
❸ $\triangle ABC$ is an isosceles triangle.	❸ $AC = BC = R$ (Step 2).
❹ $\angle\beta \cong \angle\gamma$.	❹ The angles opposite to the congr. sides of an isosceles triangle are congr. (We demonstrated this in Proof 10.) In $\triangle ABC$, $AC = BC$.
❺ $m\angle\beta + m\angle\gamma + m\angle\theta = 180°$.	❺ Angle sum thm. for triangle $\triangle ABC$.
❻ $2(m\angle\beta) + m\angle\theta = 180°$.	❻ Sub. Step 4 into Step 5 and simplify.
❼ $m\angle\beta + m\angle\alpha = 90°$.	❼ Compl. angles. The tangent line is perpendicular to radius $\overline{AC}$.
❽ $m\angle\beta + \frac{m\angle\theta}{2} = 90°$.	❽ Divide both sides of Step 6 by 2.
❾ $m\angle\beta + m\angle\alpha = m\angle\beta + \frac{m\angle\theta}{2}$.	❾ Set Eq.'s 7 and 8 equal to each other.
❿ $m\angle\alpha = \frac{m\angle\theta}{2}$. ∎	❿ Subtract $m\angle\beta$ from both sides of Step 9. ∎

Solution to Proof #47.

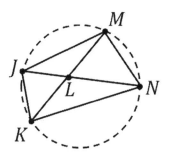

❶ ∠JLK ≅ ∠MLN.	❶ Vertical angles.
❷ ∠JKM ≅ ∠MNJ.	❷ They are both inscribed angles that intercept the same arc length (between points J and M).
❸ ΔJKL~ΔLMN. ∎	❸ Two angles are congr. (Steps 1-2). ∎

Notes:

- In Proof 43, we showed that the angular measure of an inscribed angle is one-half the angular measure of a central angle that intercepts the same arc length. It follows that any two inscribed angles that intercept the same arc length are congruent (because the angular measure of each inscribed angle is one-half the angular measure of a central angle that intercepts the same arc length).

- When two angles are congruent, the triangles are similar. (The third angle is also congruent according to the angle sum theorem.)

- It could be shown that ∠KJN ≅ ∠KMN since these are both inscribed angles that intercept the arc between points K and N.

Solution to Proof #48.

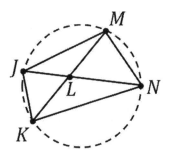

❶ $\triangle JKL \sim \triangle LMN$.	❶ We showed this in Proof 47.
❷ $JK:JL:KL = MN:LM:LN$.	❷ Corresponding sides of similar triangles come in the same proportions.
❸ $\frac{JL}{KL} = \frac{LM}{LN}$.	❸ $JL:KL = LM:LN$ (Step 2).
❹ $JL \cdot LN = KL \cdot LM$. ∎	❹ Cross multiply in Step 3. ∎

Notes:

- $\overline{JK}$ corresponds to $\overline{MN}$ because they are opposite to congruent angles $\angle JLK$ and $\angle MLN$ (which are vertical angles).

- $\overline{JL}$ corresponds to $\overline{LM}$ because they are opposite to congruent angles $\angle JKL$ and $\angle MNL$ (see Proof 47).

- $\overline{KL}$ corresponds to $\overline{LN}$ because they are opposite to congruent angles $\angle KJL$ and $\angle NML$ (see the notes to Proof 47).

- Note that $JL \cdot LN = KL \cdot LM$ (Step 4) involves multiplication, whereas $JL:KL = LM:LN$ (Step 3) involves ratios (which is division). The distinction between one dot (·) and two dots (:) makes a very significant difference.

Solution to Proof #49.

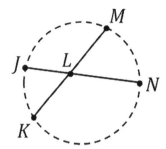 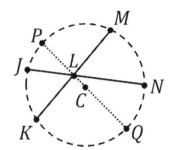

❶ $JL \cdot LN = KL \cdot LM$.

❷ $JL \cdot LN = LP \cdot LQ$.

❸ $LP = CP - LC$.

❹ $LQ = CQ + LC$.

❺ The center of the circle is at point C.

❻ $CP = CQ = R$.

❼ $LP = R - LC$.

❽ $LQ = R + LC$.

❾ $LP \cdot LQ = (R - LC)(R + LC)$.

❿ $LP \cdot LQ = R^2 - LC^2$.

⓫ $JL \cdot LN = KL \cdot LM = R^2 - LC^2$. ∎

❶ We showed this in Proof 48.

❷ Apply the result of Proof 48 to quadrilateral $JPNQ$ instead of $JMNK$.

❸ Prop. of subtraction.

❹ Prop. of addition.

❺ Given.

❻ A radius extends from point C to the edge of the circle.

❼ Sub. Step 6 into Step 3.

❽ Sub. Step 6 into Step 4.

❾ Sub. Steps 7-8 into $LP \cdot LQ$.

❿ Algebra: $(x - y)(x + y) = x^2 - y^2$.

⓫ Combine Steps 1, 2, and 10. ∎

Solution to Proof #50.

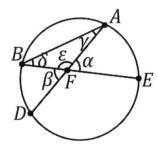 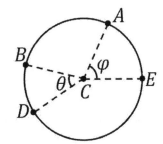

❶ $m\angle\gamma + m\angle\delta + m\angle\varepsilon = 180°$.	❶ Angle sum thm. for triangle $\triangle ABF$.
❷ $m\angle\alpha + m\angle\varepsilon = 180°$.	❷ Suppl. angles.
❸ $m\angle\gamma + m\angle\delta + m\angle\varepsilon = m\angle\alpha + m\angle\varepsilon$.	❸ Set Eq.'s 1 and 2 equal to each other.
❹ $m\angle\gamma + m\angle\delta = m\angle\alpha$.	❹ Subtract $m\angle\varepsilon$ from both sides of Step 3.
❺ $m\angle\gamma = \frac{m\angle\theta}{2}$. $\quad m\angle\delta = \frac{m\angle\varphi}{2}$.	❺ The ang. meas. of an inscribed angle is half the ang. meas. of a central angle that intercepts the same arc length. We showed this in Proof 43.
❻ $\frac{m\angle\theta}{2} + \frac{m\angle\varphi}{2} = m\angle\alpha$.	❻ Sub. Step 5 into Step 4.
❼ $\frac{m\angle\theta + m\angle\varphi}{2} = m\angle\alpha$. ∎	❼ Factor out the one-half in Step 6. ∎

Solution to Proof #51.

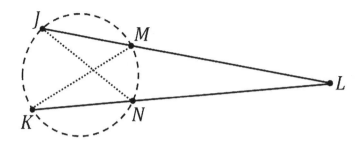

❶ ∠JLK is common to ΔJLN and ΔKLM.	❶ Reflexive prop.
❷ ∠LJN ≅ ∠LKM.	❷ They are both inscribed angles that intercept the same arc length (between points M and N).
❸ ΔJLN~ΔKLM. ∎	❸ Two angles are congr. (Steps 1-2). ∎

Notes:

- In Proof 43, we showed that the angular measure of an inscribed angle is one-half the angular measure of a central angle that intercepts the same arc length. It follows that any two inscribed angles that intercept the same arc length are congruent (because the angular measure of each inscribed angle is one-half the angular measure of a central angle that intercepts the same arc length).

- When two angles are congruent, the triangles are similar. (The third angle is also congruent according to the angle sum theorem.)

Solution to Proof #52.

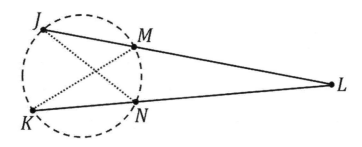

❶ $\triangle JLN \sim \triangle KLM$.	❶ We showed this in Proof 51.
❷ $LJ: LN: NJ = LK: LM: MK$.	❷ Corresponding sides of similar triangles come in the same proportions.
❸ $\frac{LJ}{LN} = \frac{LK}{LM}$.	❸ $LJ: LN = LK: LM$ (Step 2).
❹ $LJ \cdot LM = LK \cdot LN$. ■	❹ Cross multiply in Step 3. ■

Notes:

- $\overline{LM}$ corresponds to $\overline{LN}$ because they are opposite to congruent angles $\angle LKM$ and $\angle LJN$ (Proof 51).

- $\overline{NJ}$ corresponds to $\overline{MK}$ because they are opposite to the same angle ($\angle JLK$).

- Note that $LJ \cdot LM = LK \cdot LN$ (Step 4) involves multiplication, whereas $LJ: LN = LK: LM$ (Step 3) involves ratios (which is division). The distinction between one dot (·) and two dots (:) makes a very significant difference.

Solution to Proof #53.

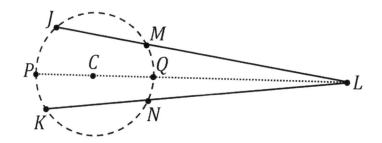

❶ $JL \cdot LM = LK \cdot LN$.	❶ We showed this in Proof 52.
❷ $JL \cdot LM = LQ \cdot LP$.	❷ Apply the result of Proof 52 to secants $\overline{LJ}$ and $\overline{LP}$ instead of secants $\overline{LJ}$ and $\overline{LK}$.
❸ $LP = LC + CP$.	❸ Prop. of addition.
❹ $LQ = LC - CQ$.	❹ Prop. of subtraction.
❺ The center of the circle is at point C.	❺ Given.
❻ $CP = CQ = R$.	❻ A radius extends from point C to the edge of the circle.
❼ $LP = LC + R$.	❼ Sub. Step 6 into Step 3.
❽ $LQ = LC - R$.	❽ Sub. Step 6 into Step 4.
❾ $LQ \cdot LP = (LC - R)(LC + R)$.	❾ Sub. Steps 7-8 into $LQ \cdot LP$.
❿ $LQ \cdot LP = LC^2 - R^2$.	❿ Algebra: $(x - y)(x + y) = x^2 - y^2$.
⓫ $JL \cdot LM = LK \cdot LN = LC^2 - R^2$. ■	⓫ Combine Steps 1, 2, and 10. ■

Solution to Proof #54.

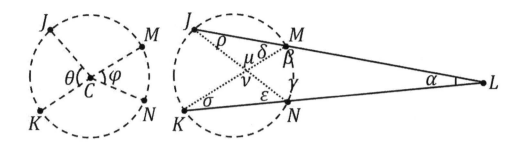

❶ $m\angle\alpha + m\angle\beta + m\angle\sigma = 180°$.	❶ Angle sum thm. for triangle ΔLMK.
❷ $m\angle\delta + m\angle\beta = 180°$.	❷ Suppl. angles.
❸ $m\angle\alpha + m\angle\beta + m\angle\sigma = m\angle\delta + m\angle\beta$.	❸ Set Eq.'s 1 and 2 equal to each other.
❹ $m\angle\alpha + m\angle\sigma = m\angle\delta$.	❹ Subtract $m\angle\beta$ from both sides of Step 3.
❺ $m\angle\sigma = \frac{m\angle\varphi}{2}$. $m\angle\delta = \frac{m\angle\theta}{2}$.	❺ The ang. meas. of an inscribed angle is half the ang. meas. of a central angle that intercepts the same arc length. We showed this in Proof 43.
❻ $m\angle\alpha + \frac{m\angle\varphi}{2} = \frac{m\angle\theta}{2}$.	❻ Sub. Step 5 into Step 4.
❼ $m\angle\alpha = \frac{m\angle\theta}{2} - \frac{m\angle\varphi}{2}$.	❼ Subtract $\frac{m\angle\varphi}{2}$ from both sides of Step 6.
❽ $m\angle\alpha = \frac{m\angle\theta - m\angle\varphi}{2}$. ∎	❽ Factor out the one-half in Step 7. ∎

Solution to Proof #55.

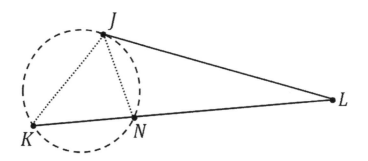

❶ $\angle JLK$ is common to ΔJLN and ΔKLJ.	❶ Reflexive prop.
❷ $\overline{JL}$ is a tangent.	❷ Given.
❸ $\overline{JN}$ is a chord.	❸ Def. of chord.
❹ $\angle LJN$ is formed by a tangent and chord.	❹ Follows from Steps 2-3.
❺ $m\angle LJN = \frac{m\angle \theta}{2}$.	❺ We showed this in Proof 46, where $\angle \theta$ is a central angle intercepting the arc length between J and N.
❻ $m\angle JKN = \frac{m\angle \theta}{2}$.	❻ We showed this in Proof 43. This is an inscribed angle intercepting the arc length between J and N.
❼ $\angle LJN \cong \angle JKL$.	❼ Combine Steps 5-6.
❽ $\Delta JLN \sim \Delta KLJ$. ∎	❽ Two angles are congr. (Steps 1 and 7). ∎

Solution to Proof #56.

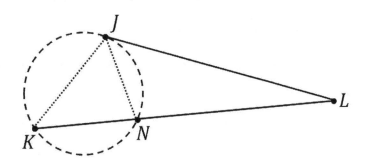

❶ $\triangle JLN \sim \triangle KLJ$.	❶ We showed this in Proof 55.
❷ $LJ:LN:NJ = LK:LJ:JK$.	❷ Corresponding sides of similar triangles come in the same proportions.
❸ $\frac{LJ}{LN} = \frac{LK}{LJ}$.	❸ $LJ:LN = LK:LJ$ (Step 2).
❹ $LJ^2 = LN \cdot LK$. ∎	❹ Cross multiply in Step 3. ∎

Notes:

- $\overline{LJ}$ of $\triangle KLJ$ corresponds to $\overline{LN}$ of $\triangle JLN$ because they are opposite to congruent angles $\angle JKL$ and $\angle LJN$ (Proof 55).
- $\overline{NJ}$ corresponds to $\overline{JK}$ because they are opposite to the same angle ($\angle JLK$).
- Note that $LJ^2 = LN \cdot LK$ (Step 4) involves multiplication, whereas $LJ:LN = LK:LJ$ (Step 3) involves ratios (which is division). The distinction between one dot ($\cdot$) and two dots ($:$) makes a very significant difference.

Solution to Proof #57.

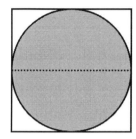

❶ The radius of the circle is R.

❶ Given.

❷ The square has edge length L.

❷ Given.

❸ The horizontal diameter shown above passes through the center of the circle.

❸ Def. of diameter.

❹ The horizontal diameter is perp. to the tangent lines.

❹ Tangent lines and diameters are perpendicular at the point where they intersect.

❺ The square's interior angles are right angles.

❺ Def. of square.

❻ The horizontal diameter divides the square into two rectangles.

❻ The interior angles of these quad.'s are right angles. (Combine Steps 4-5.)

❼ The width of each rectangle is L.

❼ Same width as the square.

❽ The width of each rectangle is D.

❽ Step 3.

❾ $L = D$.

❾ Combine Steps 7-8.

❿ $D = 2R$.

❿ The diameter is twice the radius.

⓫ $L = 2R$. ∎

⓫ Combine Steps 9-10. ∎

Solution to Proof #58.

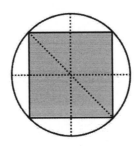

❶ The radius of the circle is R.	❶ Given.
❷ The square has edge length L.	❷ Given.
❸ The diagonal line shown above cuts the square into congr. 45°-45°-90° triangles.	❸ Prop.'s of a square. The diagonals of a square bisect the interior angles. The interior angles of a square are right angles. A square has congruent edges.
❹ The diagonal of the square is a diameter of the circle.	❹ Apply the midsegment theorem (Proof 19) to the triangles. The horizontal, vertical, and diagonal lines intersect at the same point (the center of the circle).
❺ $L^2 + L^2 = H^2$.	❺ P.T. (where H = hypotenuse).
❻ $2L^2 = H^2$.	❻ $L^2 + L^2 = 2L^2$.
❼ $L\sqrt{2} = H$.	❼ Squareroot both sides of Step 6.
❽ $H = D$.	❽ Step 4 expressed with symbols.
❾ $D = 2R$.	❾ The diameter is twice the radius.
❿ $L\sqrt{2} = 2R$.	❿ Combine Steps 7-9 together.
⓫ $L = \frac{2R}{\sqrt{2}} = R\sqrt{2}$. ∎	⓫ $\frac{2}{\sqrt{2}} = \sqrt{2}$ because $\sqrt{2}\sqrt{2} = 2$. ∎

Solution to Proof #59.

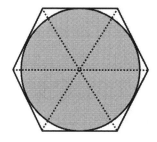 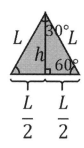

❶ The radius of the circle is R.	❶ Given.
❷ The hexagon is regular and has edge length L.	❷ Given.
❸ The regular hexagon can be cut into 6 congr. equilateral triangles as shown above.	❸ We showed this in Proof 38.
❹ The interior angles of the equilateral triangles have ang. meas.'s of 60°.	❹ Prop. of equilateral triangle.
❺ Each equilateral triangle can be cut into two 30°-60°-90° triangles as shown above on the right.	❺ We showed this in Proof 16.
❻ The height of each equilateral triangle is $\frac{L\sqrt{3}}{2}$.	❻ See the solutions to Proofs 16-17.
❼ The heights of the two center triangles add up to the diameter of the circle.	❼ Draw a vertical diameter to see this.
❽ $D = 2\left(\frac{L\sqrt{3}}{2}\right) = L\sqrt{3}$.	❽ Combine Steps 6-7 together.
❾ $D = 2R$.	❾ The diameter is twice the radius.
❿ $2R = L\sqrt{3}$.	❿ Combine Steps 8-9 together.
⓫ $L = \frac{2R}{\sqrt{3}} = \frac{2R\sqrt{3}}{3}$. ∎	⓫ $\frac{1}{\sqrt{3}} = \frac{1}{\sqrt{3}}\frac{\sqrt{3}}{\sqrt{3}} = \frac{\sqrt{3}}{3}$ because $\sqrt{3}\sqrt{3} = 3$. ∎

Solution to Proof #60.

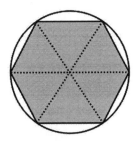

❶ The radius of the circle is R.	❶ Given.
❷ The hexagon is regular and has edge length L.	❷ Given.
❸ The regular hexagon can be cut into 6 congr. equilateral triangles as shown above.	❸ We showed this in Proof 38.
❹ The interior angles of the equilateral triangles have ang. meas.'s of 60°.	❹ Prop. of equilateral triangle.
❺ Each equilateral triangle has edge length L.	❺ Each equilateral triangle shares an edge with the regular hexagon.
❻ The bases of the top left and top right triangles add up to the diameter of the circle.	❻ They form a horizontal diameter, as shown above.
❼ $D = 2L$.	❼ Combine Steps 5-6 together.
❽ $D = 2R$.	❽ The diameter is twice the radius.
❾ $2R = 2L$.	❾ Combine Steps 7-8 together.
❿ $L = R$. ∎	❿ Divide both sides of Step 9 by 2. ∎

Solution to Proof #61.

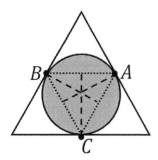

❶ The radius of the circle is R.

❶ Given.

❷ The triangle is equilateral and has edge length L.

❷ Given.

❸ The equilateral triangle can be cut into 4 congr. equilateral triangles as shown above.

❸ Apply Proof 20 to achieve this. Proof 18 will then show that they are similar to the large triangle.

❹ The small equilateral triangles have edge length $\frac{L}{2}$.

❹ The edges of two small triangles form one edge of the large one.

❺ The height of each equilateral triangle is $\frac{\sqrt{3}}{2}\left(\frac{L}{2}\right) = \frac{L\sqrt{3}}{4}$.

❺ See the solutions to Proofs 16-17. Use Step 4 for the edge length.

❻ The central triangle's medians intersect at its centroid, 2/3 the dist. from a vertex to its opp. midpoint.

❻ See the solution to Proof 21 and the notes to its solution.

❼ $\frac{2}{3}\left(\frac{L\sqrt{3}}{4}\right) = \frac{L\sqrt{3}}{6}$ = the dist. of Step 6.

❼ Take two-thirds of Step 5.

❽ The centroid of the central triangle lies at the center of the circle.

❽ Points A, B, and C are equidistant from the centroid and center.

❾ $R = \frac{L\sqrt{3}}{6}$.

❾ Combine Steps 7-8 together.

❿ $L = \frac{6R}{\sqrt{3}} = 2R\sqrt{3}$. ∎

❿ Algebra. Note that $\frac{6}{\sqrt{3}} = \frac{6}{\sqrt{3}}\frac{\sqrt{3}}{\sqrt{3}} = \frac{6\sqrt{3}}{3} = 2\sqrt{3}$ because $\sqrt{3}\sqrt{3} = 3$. ∎

Solution to Proof #62.

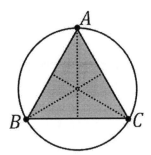

❶ The radius of the circle is R.

❷ The triangle is equilateral and has edge length L.

❸ The height of each equilateral triangle is $\frac{L\sqrt{3}}{2}$.

❹ The triangle's medians intersect at its centroid, 2/3 the dist. from a vertex to its opp. midpoint.

❺ $\frac{2}{3}\left(\frac{L\sqrt{3}}{2}\right) = \frac{L\sqrt{3}}{3}$ = the dist. of Step 4.

❻ The centroid of the triangle lies at the center of the circle.

❼ $R = \frac{L\sqrt{3}}{3}$.

❽ $L = \frac{3R}{\sqrt{3}} = R\sqrt{3}$. ■

❶ Given.

❷ Given.

❸ See the solutions to Proofs 16-17.

❹ See the solution to Proof 21 and the notes to its solution.

❺ Take two-thirds of Step 3.

❻ Points A, B, and C are equidistant from the centroid and center.

❼ Combine Steps 5-6 together.

❽ Algebra. Note that $\frac{3}{\sqrt{3}} = \frac{3}{\sqrt{3}}\frac{\sqrt{3}}{\sqrt{3}} = \frac{3\sqrt{3}}{3} = \sqrt{3}$ because $\sqrt{3}\sqrt{3} = 3$. ■

Solution to Proof #63.

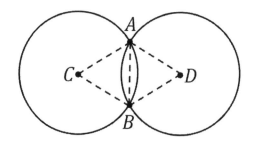

❶ The radius of each circle is R.

❷ $AB = R$.

❸ The centers lie at C and D.

❹ $AC = BC = AD = BD = R$.

❺ The two triangles shown above are equilateral.

❻ The height of each equilateral triangle is $\frac{R\sqrt{3}}{2}$.

❼ CD = twice the height.

❽ $CD = R\sqrt{3}$. ∎

❶ Given.

❷ Given.

❸ Given.

❹ A radius extends from C or D to the edge of the corresponding circle.

❺ All three sides are congruent (Steps 2 and 4).

❻ See the solutions to Proofs 16-17. Note that the edge length is R.

❼ Turn the page sideways such that AB is the base.

❽ Multiply Step 6 by 2. ∎

Solution to Proof #64.

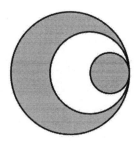

❶ The radii are R, $2R$, and $3R$.

❷ The area of each individual circle is πR^2, $\pi(2R)^2 = 4\pi R^2$, and $\pi(3R)^2 = 9\pi R^2$.

❸ The area of the shaded region equals the area of the large circle minus the area of the middle circle plus the area of the small circle.

❹ The area of the unshaded region equals the area of the middle circle minus the area of the small circle.

❺ $A_{shaded} = 9\pi R^2 - 4\pi R^2 + \pi R^2$.
$A_{unshaded} = 4\pi R^2 - \pi R^2$.

❻ $A_{shaded} = 6\pi R^2$.
$A_{unshaded} = 3\pi R^2$.

❼ $\dfrac{A_{shaded}}{A_{unshaded}} = \dfrac{6\pi R^2}{3\pi R^2} = \dfrac{6}{3} = 2.$ ∎

❶ These ratios are given.

❷ Formula for the area of a circle. Use the radii from Step 1. Note that $(ab)^2 = a^2 b^2$.

❸ The area of a region equals the sum of the areas of its non-overlapping parts.

❹ The area of a region equals the sum of the areas of its non-overlapping parts.

❺ Steps 3-4 expressed algebraically.

❻ Simplify Step 5.
$9 - 4 + 1 = 6$ and $4 - 1 = 3$.

❼ Divide Step 5 by Step 6. ∎

WAS THIS BOOK HELPFUL?

A great deal of effort and thought was put into this book, such as:
- Careful selection of problems for their instructional value.
- Numerous illustrations to help visualize the principles.
- Introductory chapters review the terminology and ideas.
- Ample examples to help illustrate the strategies and concepts.

If you appreciate the effort that went into making this book possible, there is a simple way that you could show it:

Please take a moment to post an honest review.

For example, you can review this book at Amazon.com or Barnes & Noble's website at BN.com.

Even a short review can be helpful and will be much appreciated. If you're not sure what to write, following are a few ideas, though it's best to describe what's important to you.
- Were the introductory chapters helpful?
- Did you enjoy the selection of problems?
- Were you able to understand the solutions?
- How much did you learn from reading and using this workbook?
- Would you recommend this book to others? If so, why?

Do you believe that you found a mistake? Please email the author, Chris McMullen, at greekphysics@yahoo.com to ask about it. One of two things will happen:
- You might discover that it wasn't a mistake after all and learn why.
- You might be right, in which case the author will be grateful and future readers will benefit from the correction. Everyone is human.

ABOUT THE AUTHOR

Dr. Chris McMullen has over 20 years of experience teaching university physics in California, Oklahoma, Pennsylvania, and Louisiana. Dr. McMullen is also an author of math and science workbooks. Whether in the classroom or as a writer, Dr. McMullen loves sharing knowledge and the art of motivating and engaging students.

The author earned his Ph.D. in phenomenological high-energy physics (particle physics) from Oklahoma State University in 2002. Originally from California, Chris McMullen earned his Master's degree from California State University, Northridge, where his thesis was in the field of electron spin resonance.

As a physics teacher, Dr. McMullen observed that many students lack fluency in fundamental math skills. In an effort to help students of all ages and levels master basic math skills, he published a series of math workbooks on arithmetic, fractions, long division, algebra, trigonometry, and calculus entitled *Improve Your Math Fluency*. Dr. McMullen has also published a variety of science books, including introductions to basic astronomy and chemistry concepts in addition to physics workbooks.

Author, Chris McMullen, Ph.D.

For students who need to improve their algebra skills:

- Isolating the unknown
- Quadratic equations
- Factoring
- Cross multiplying
- Systems of equations
- Straight line graphs
- Word problems

www.improveyourmathfluency.com

MATH

This series of math workbooks is geared toward practicing essential math skills:

- Algebra and trigonometry
- Calculus
- Fractions, decimals, and percentages
- Long division
- Multiplication and division
- Addition and subtraction

www.improveyourmathfluency.com

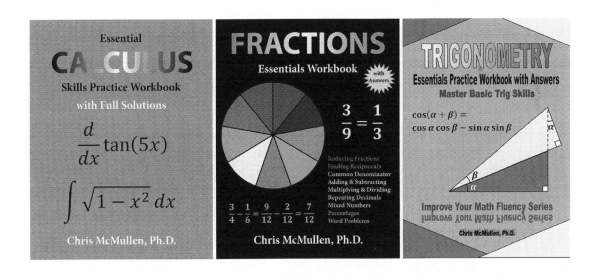

PUZZLES

The author of this book, Chris McMullen, enjoys solving puzzles. His favorite puzzle is Kakuro (kind of like a cross between crossword puzzles and Sudoku). He once taught a three-week summer course on puzzles. If you enjoy mathematical pattern puzzles, you might appreciate:

300+ Mathematical Pattern Puzzles

Number Pattern Recognition & Reasoning

- Pattern recognition
- Visual discrimination
- Analytical skills
- Logic and reasoning
- Analogies
- Mathematics

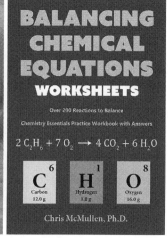

SCIENCE

Dr. McMullen has published a variety of **science** books, including:

- Basic astronomy concepts
- Basic chemistry concepts
- Balancing chemical reactions
- Calculus-based physics textbooks
- Calculus-based physics workbooks
- Calculus-based physics examples
- Trig-based physics workbooks
- Trig-based physics examples
- Creative physics problems
- Modern physics

www.monkeyphysicsblog.wordpress.com

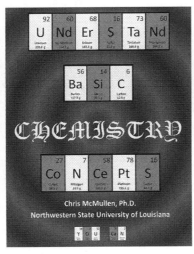

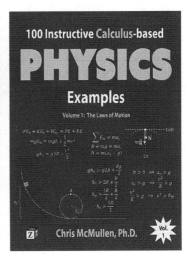

THE FOURTH DIMENSION

Are you curious about a possible fourth dimension of space?

- Explore the world of hypercubes and hyperspheres.
- Imagine living in a two-dimensional world.
- Try to understand the fourth dimension by analogy.
- Several illustrations help to try to visualize a fourth dimension of space.
- Investigate hypercube patterns.
- What would it be like to be a four-dimensional being living in a four-dimensional world?
- Learn about the physics of a possible four-dimensional universe.

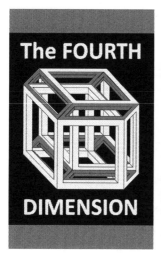
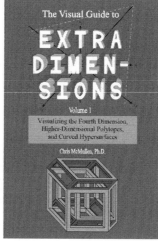
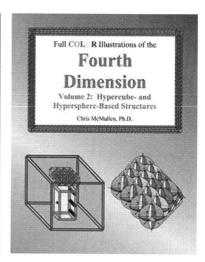

Made in the USA
Middletown, DE
25 September 2021